Nelson Advanced Modular Science

Fields

MARK ELLSE • CHRIS HONEYWILL

with a contribution by David Hartley

Nelson

Thomas Nelson & Sons Ltd
Nelson House
Mayfield Road
Walton-on-Thames
Surrey KT12 5PL
United Kingdom

I(T)P® Thomas Nelson is an International Thomson Company

I(T)P® is used under licence

First published by Thomas Nelson & Sons Ltd 1998

ISBN   0 17 448263 9
9 8 7 6 5 4 3 2 1
01 00 99 98

Picture Research by Image Select International
Design/Typesetting by Hardlines, Park Street, Charlbury, Oxfordshire
Printed in Croatia by Zrinski Printing and Publishing House, Cakovec

Publishing team:
Acquisitions: Sonia Clark
Staff editorial: Simon Bell
Freelance editorial: Geoff Amor
Production: Suzanne Howarth

Contents

Acknowledgements

The authors and publishers are grateful for the kind assistance of John Warren for his painstaking work in reading and commenting on the manuscripts. They are also grateful to Dr Stephen Kukureca and Dr M.L.H. Wise of the School of Metallurgy and Materials, University of Birmingham, for giving specialist advice on the Solid Materials Topic, Dr N. Mason of the Department of Physics, University College London, for giving specialist advice on the Earth and Atmosphere Topic, and Dr Jonathan Allday of The King's School, Canterbury, and Susan Oldcorn for giving specialist advice on the Particle Physics Topic.

David Hartley has painstakingly read through and commented in detail on the manuscripts of the whole series. He also wrote the Particle Physics Topic for this volume. The authors gratefully acknowledge his major contribution to the success of the whole series.

The authors and publishers are grateful to the following for permission to reproduce copyright photographs:

Peter Gould: figures 1.1, 1.2, 2.3, 6.1, 6.3, 9.6(a), 10.1 (top, centre and bottom), 10.4, 12.1, 14.1, 15.3, 19.1, M16, M31 (top and bottom)

Andy Ross: figure M18

Science Photo Library: figures 3.2, M1, M5, M20, M34, E1, E20, E28, E29, P1, P3, P6, P24

British Aerospace Airbus Ltd.: figures M27 and M28

The authors and publishers are grateful to Edexcel London Examinations for permission to reproduce all the examination questions used in this book.

Preface

This book takes you through the fourth Module of the Edexcel London Examinations A-level Physics syllabus. It is also suitable for the core content of other A-level schemes. We have divided the book into small chapters, each of which introduces only a few new ideas.

Within the chapters are suggestions for experiments. You may not do or see all the experiments, but you should think about them as you read the text and try to predict what the experiments would show. Most of the experiments are described in a way that you could use yourself as an answer to an examination question that required an experimental description.

Important terms are highlighted in **bold**. There is a list of these terms, under the heading 'Things you need to know' on pages 105–106 of this book.

On pages 91–95 you will find practice questions to try after studying each chapter. There is also a selection of past examination questions.

The chapters are in a possible teaching order, but as far as possible we have tried to make them self-contained so that you can use them in any order, or dip into them for revision.

This book is one of a series of four Module texts for Edexcel London Examinations A-level Physics.

Alongside them is published a set of Experiment Sheets by Adrian Watt which describe in greater detail how to carry out many of the experiments in the texts. There is also a Teacher's Guide, showing how the different publications relate to the examination syllabus and giving guidance on apparatus.

Mark Ellse is Director of Chase Academy, Cannock, Staffordshire, and a Principal Examiner for Edexcel London Examinations.

Chris Honeywill is former Deputy Registrar and Head of Physics at The Sixth Form College, Farnborough, Hampshire, and is an Assistant Principal Examiner for Edexcel London Examinations.

1 Gravitational fields

Figure 1.1 A 55 kg woman and a 70 kg man

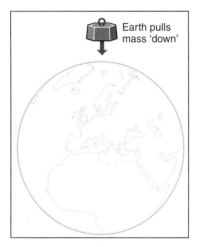

Figure 1.3 The mass accelerates because of the single force on it

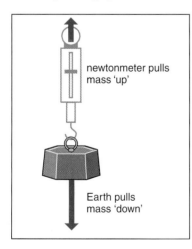

Figure 1.4 The force of the newtonmeter is equal to the weight

Mass

The **mass** of a body is the amount of matter in that body. Mass is a base quantity measured in kilograms. The man and woman in Figure 1.1 are about average size; their masses are about 70 kg for the man and 55 kg for the woman. Mass is a scalar quantity – it has no direction associated with it.

The mass of a body does not vary from place to place. The masses of the two people in Figure 1.1 are always the same, whether on the Earth, on the Moon, or floating about in outer space.

Measuring weight

- Hang a 1 kg mass on a newton spring balance (Figure 1.2). Measure the force required to support the mass.
- Repeat with masses of 0.5 kg and 2 kg.
- What is the resultant force on the mass when it is hanging on the end of the balance? Draw a free-body force diagram for the mass.

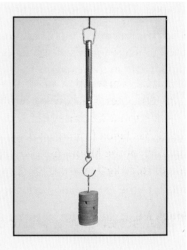

Figure 1.2 The weight of 1 kg is 9.8 N

Weight

If you release a body near the Earth, it accelerates towards the Earth, because the Earth exerts a gravitational force on the body (Figure 1.3). This gravitational force is the body's **weight**.

When you hang a body on a spring balance, the spring balance provides the upward force to support the body. The force of the balance on the body is equal and opposite to the weight, as shown in Figure 1.4. The resultant of this contact force from the balance and the weight is zero, so the body is in equilibrium. It hangs at rest from the balance.

Gravitational fields

Physicists use the word **field**, or **force field**, for a region in which forces act. Any mass near the Earth experiences a force of gravity towards the Earth. This region, where the Earth exerts a gravitational force on a mass, is the Earth's **gravitational field**. Other bodies have gravitational fields. The Sun's gravitational field is responsible for the orbits of the planets. The Moon's gravitational field affects the tides on Earth.

Gravitational field strength

In the experiment above, you learnt that the Earth pulls harder on large masses than on small ones. The weight of an object depends on the mass of that object. Near the Earth's surface, the Earth pulls on each kilogram with a force of about 9.8 N, and proportionately more or less on larger or smaller masses.

The **gravitational field strength** (g) is the force exerted by a gravitational field on each kilogram. Near the Earth the gravitational field strength is about 9.8 N kg^{-1}. So

weight = mass × gravitational field strength $F = mg$

For a woman of mass 55 kg near the Earth,

$$F = mg = 55 \text{ kg} \times 9.8 \text{ N kg}^{-1} = 540 \text{ N}$$

Her weight on Earth is 540 N.

The Earth's gravitational field strength depends on distance from the Earth. As you get higher, the field strength gets less. If you take an accurate spring balance and a 1 kg mass from sea level to a height of 8 km, you can measure that g has fallen from an average value of 9.81 N kg^{-1} to 9.78 N kg^{-1}. At the distance of the Moon, the gravitational field strength of the Earth has dropped to 0.0028 N kg^{-1}. You can see how to calculate this value in Chapter 4.

Field strength and acceleration

You know from *Mechanics and Electricity* that a body in free fall near the Earth accelerates at a rate of about 9.8 m s^{-2}. It is not a coincidence that this is the same numerical value as the gravitational field strength.

The mass in Figure 1.3 is falling freely. It has only its weight acting on it:

weight = mass × gravitational field strength

The body's acceleration can be calculated from Newton's second law:

force (the weight) = mass × acceleration

So equating these two equations gives

mass × gravitational field strength = mass × acceleration

gravitational field strength = acceleration

$$g = a$$

You can show that the units of g and a are the same. The unit of g is N kg^{-1} = (kg m s^{-2}) kg^{-1} = m s^{-2}, which is the unit of a.

Newton's law of gravitation

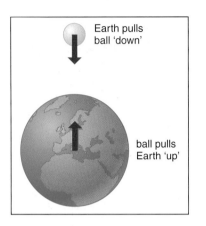

Figure 2.1 *The Earth attracts the ball, and the ball attracts the Earth*

Mutual attraction

It is no great surprise that a body has weight: the Earth pulls the body down. But it is not so obvious that the body also pulls the Earth up with an equal and opposite force. Figure 2.1 shows the forces between a ball and the Earth. You studied this situation in Chapters 9 and 10 of *Mechanics and Electricity*.

Weight, a gravitational force, is not a single force acting on one object, but one of a pair of forces that act between two objects. Gravitational forces are the result of *mutual* attraction, where two objects both attract each other.

Isaac Newton suggested theories about gravitation based on astronomical observations. He suggested that gravitational forces occur between all pairs of bodies. There are gravitational forces between you and this book, as well as between this book and the Earth (Figure 2.2).

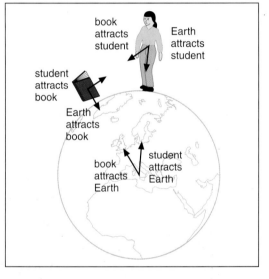

Figure 2.2 *There are forces between you and the book, as well as between the Earth and the book*

Investigating the forces between two masses
- Place a lead mass on top of a sensitive balance and note the reading.
- Observe the balance reading as you bring up another lead mass supported from a retort stand (Figure 2.3).
- Comment on the size of the gravitational forces between the two masses.

Figure 2.3 *Any change in the balance reading shows the force between the two masses*

Newton's law of gravitation

Newton's law of gravitation states that every mass attracts every other mass. The force of attraction is proportional to each of the masses and inversely proportional to the square of the distances apart:

$$F = GmM/r^2$$

where F is the force, m and M the two masses and r the distance apart (Figure 2.4). G is a constant that applies in all situations of gravitational attraction. It is called the **universal gravitational constant**. Its value is 6.67×10^{-11} N m^2 kg^{-2}.

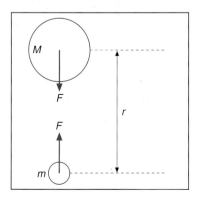

Figure 2.4 *Every mass attracts every other mass*

Newton's law of gravitation applies to all spherical masses if you measure the distance apart between their centres of mass. The law also applies to non-spherical masses if their distance apart is large compared with the size of the masses.

Estimate the gravitational force between the two people, masses 55 kg and 70 kg, in Figure 1.1 if they stand with their centres of mass 0.75 m apart.
We get

$$F = GmM/r^2$$

$$= 6.67 \times 10^{-11} \, \text{N m}^2 \, \text{kg}^{-2} \times 55 \, \text{kg} \times 70 \, \text{kg}/(0.75 \, \text{m})^2$$

$$= 4.6 \times 10^{-7} \, \text{N} = 0.47 \, \mu\text{N}$$

Worked example

Measuring G

Newton's law of gravitation predicts that gravitational force decreases if the objects are further apart. If you are a long way from the Earth, your weight is less, because the gravitational force is less.

If one or both masses are small, the gravitational forces of attraction are small. The attractive force between a pair of masses in the laboratory is far too small to measure with an electronic top-pan balance.

Over a hundred years after Newton proposed his law, Henry Cavendish devised the first practical method of measuring the gravitational force between masses. He attached two small lead masses to a bar and hung it from a long thin wire (Figure 2.5). As well as supporting the bar and masses, the wire acted like a very weak spring, rotating the bar back to its equilibrium position. He recorded the equilibrium position of the bar. Then he placed two larger lead masses in the positions shown. They attracted the masses on the bar, and caused it to rotate slightly against the restoring force from the wire. He measured the angle through which the bar rotated, and from this calculated the force between the masses. By measuring the forces, the masses and their distances apart, he calculated G.

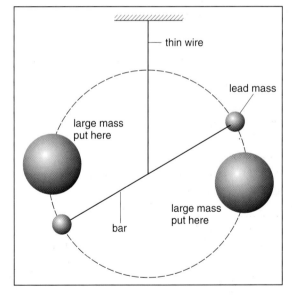

Cavendish realised that measuring G allowed him to calculate the mass of the Earth. Think about a 1 kg mass on the Earth's surface. The weight of this mass is 9.8 N and, since the radius of the Earth is 6400 km, it is this distance from the centre of the Earth.
So rewriting the equation $F = G/mMr^2$ gives

Figure 2.5 Cavendish's method

$$M = Fr^2/Gm$$

$$= 9.8 \, \text{N} \times (6.4 \times 10^6 \, \text{m})^2/(6.7 \times 10^{-11} \, \text{N m}^2 \, \text{kg}^{-2} \times 1 \, \text{kg}) = 6.0 \times 10^{24} \, \text{kg}$$

Satellites

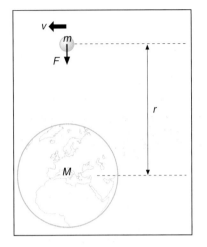

Figure 3.1 The Earth provides the centripetal force for the Moon's circular motion

Planets and satellites

You know from Chapter 21 of *Mechanics and Electricity* that a body executing circular motion needs a centripetal force. For a planet or satellite orbiting a star or planet, the gravitational attraction provides the centripetal force.

The Moon orbits the Earth. Figure 3.1 shows a free-body force diagram for the Moon. There is only one force F acting on the Moon. This is the gravitational force of the Earth (GmM/r^2), which provides the centripetal force (mv^2/r) for the Moon's circular motion. The single force on the Moon is the centripetal force and it is also the gravitational force. So the two mathematical ways of describing this force must be equal, i.e. centripetal force = gravitational force:

$$mv^2/r = GmM/r^2 \qquad \text{so} \qquad v^2/r = GM/r^2$$

The centripetal acceleration is v^2/r, and GM/r^2 is the gravitational field strength at radius r. So this last equation states that the centripetal acceleration is the gravitational field strength. You might like to compare this with the end of Chapter 1, which explained that the acceleration of free fall at a point is the gravitational field strength at that point. A satellite is in free fall. The acceleration of free fall is the gravitational field strength at that point, which accounts for the centripetal acceleration.

It is often useful to write the equations for satellite motion in terms of the angular speed ω. The centripetal force is $mr\omega^2$:

$$mr\omega^2 = GmM/r^2 \qquad \text{so} \qquad r\omega^2 = GM/r^2$$

The centripetal acceleration is $r\omega^2$, and GM/r^2 is the gravitational field strength at radius r. So again this last equation states that the centripetal acceleration is the gravitational field strength.

Figure 3.2 Nimbus, a near-Earth, polar satellite used for ozone distribution and environmental monitoring

Worked example

The period T of the Moon about the Earth is about 28 days. Calculate the radius of the Moon's orbit around the Earth, given that the mass of the Earth is 6.0×10^{24} kg and $G = 6.7 \times 10^{-11}$ N m^2 kg^{-2}.

For circular motion questions, it is often useful to find the angular velocity ω:

$$\omega = 2\pi/T = 2\pi \text{ rad}/(28 \times 24 \times 3600 \text{ s}) = 2.6 \times 10^{-6} \text{ rad s}^{-1}$$

Now we can use centripetal acceleration = gravitational field strength, i.e.

$$r\omega^2 = GM/r^2$$

$$r^3 = GM/\omega^2 = 6.7 \times 10^{-11} \text{ N m}^2 \text{ kg}^{-2} \times 6.0 \times 10^{24} \text{ kg}/(2.6 \times 10^{-6} \text{ rad s}^{-1})^2$$

$$r = \sqrt[3]{(5.95 \times 10^{25} \text{ m}^3)} = 390 \text{ Mm}$$

Kepler's law

You know that centripetal acceleration = gravitational field strength:

$$r\omega^2 = GM/r^2 \qquad \text{so} \qquad r^3\omega^2 = GM$$

But $\omega = 2\pi/T$ where T is the period of the circular motion. This gives

$$r^3(2\pi/T)^2 = GM \qquad \text{so} \qquad T^2 = (4\pi^2/GM)r^3$$

This law says that the period T of an object in gravitational circular motion depends on the mass M of the object about which it is rotating and the radius of the orbit. For the planets orbiting around the Sun, the squares of their periods are proportional to their radii cubed:

$$T^2 \propto r^3$$

This is one of a series of laws that the German astronomer Johannes Kepler discovered by analysing observations of the planets' motion. Newton based his theory of gravitation on Kepler's laws. Table 3.1 shows the periods and orbital radii of the planets.

Table 3.1 *The periods and orbital radii of the planets*

Planet	Period /Earth years	Orbital radius /Earth's orbital radius
Mercury	0.24	0.39
Venus	0.62	0.73
Earth	1.0	1.0
Mars	1.9	1.5
Jupiter	12	5.2
Saturn	29	10
Uranus	84	19
Neptune	160	30
Pluto	250	39

Satellites

An artificial satellite is an object placed into orbit around a planet, usually around the Earth. Satellites were first put into space for research. Now they are used for many purposes. Near-Earth satellites (Figure 3.2) orbit very quickly, just above the atmosphere, where g is almost the same as its value on the Earth's surface. They are used for weather observation, for mapping the ground and for spying. The period of a near-Earth satellite is about 90 min.

Geostationary (geosynchronous) satellites have a period of 24 h. They have the same period as the Earth. They orbit above the equator and keep the same position above the Earth's surface. The most important use for geostationary satellites is for telecommunications. Geostationary satellites broadcast satellite television and relay telephone conversations over wide areas of the Earth.

The radius of the orbit of a geostationary satellite is about 42×10^6 m, just over a tenth of the way from the Earth to the Moon.

Figure 3.3 shows the relative positions of the Moon and the two types of satellites above.

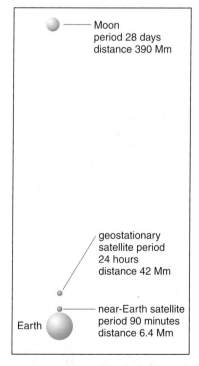

Figure 3.3 The further a satellite is from the Earth, the greater its period

4 Gravitational field lines

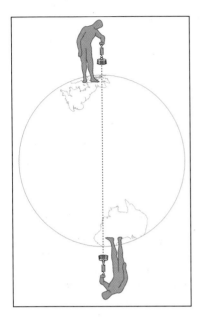

Figure 4.1 The Earth pulls masses towards its centre

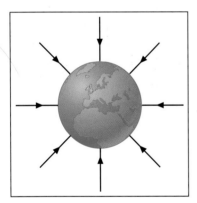

Figure 4.2 The Earth's field is radial

The shape of the Earth's field

Wherever a mass is, in England or Australia, near the ground or in space, its weight acts towards the centre of the Earth, as Figure 4.1 shows. The lines on Figure 4.2 are field lines. They show the directions of the gravitational forces at any point. The field lines are radial. They are all directed towards the centre of the Earth. Near the Earth, where the lines are close together, the field is stronger. A long way from the Earth, where the field lines are further apart, the field is weaker.

Calculating the strength of the Earth's field

If a body of mass m is a distance r from the centre of the Earth, you know from previous chapters that the weight of the body, F, is given by the formula $F = GmM/r^2$. The gravitational field strength is

$$g = F/m = (GmM/r^2)/m = GM/r^2$$

This formula allows you to calculate g at any distance from the Earth.

Figure 4.3 shows how g varies with distance from the centre of the Earth. On the surface, 6.4×10^6 m from the centre of the Earth, $g = 9.8$ N kg^{-1}. Twice as far from the centre of the Earth (12.8×10^6 m from the centre),

$$g = GM/r^2$$
$$= 6.7 \times 10^{-11} \text{ N m}^2 \text{ kg}^{-2} \times 6.0 \times 10^{24} \text{ kg}/(12.8 \times 10^6 \text{ m})^2$$
$$= 2.5 \text{ N kg}^{-1}$$

This is a quarter of the value at the Earth's surface.

Be careful to notice the difference between G and g. G does not vary. It is the universal gravitational constant, the constant of proportionality in Newton's law of gravitation. The gravitational field strength g is the gravitational field strength at a particular point. It is the force per unit mass. It varies from place to place.

Worked example

Calculate the gravitational field strength due to the Sun at the orbit of the Earth. The mass of the Sun is 2.0×10^{30} kg. The radius of the Earth's orbit is 1.5×10^{11} m.

We get

$$g = GM/r^2$$
$$= 6.7 \times 10^{-11} \text{ N m}^2 \text{ kg}^{-2} \times 2.0 \times 10^{30} \text{ kg}/(1.5 \times 10^{11} \text{ m})^2$$
$$= 6.0 \times 10^{-3} \text{ N kg}^{-1}$$

Inverse square law

You read about the **inverse square law** in Chapter 16 of *Matter and Waves*. Like gravitational force, gravitational fields follow an inverse square law; $g \propto 1/r^2$. If you double the distance from the centre of a mass, the field strength quarters. If you treble the distance, the field strength reduces to a ninth. If the distance is ten times as large, the field is a hundredth.

Figure 4.3 shows a graph of the Earth's gravitational field and how it varies with distance from the centre of the Earth.

At the Moon's orbit, a distance of 380 Mm from the Earth, the gravitational field strength is only 2.8 mN kg^{-1}, over 3000 times smaller than at the surface of the Earth. But this tiny gravitational field strength is still large enough to cause the Moon to circle round the Earth, rather than continuing in a straight line through space.

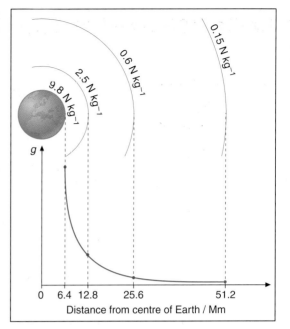

Figure 4.3 How g varies with distance from the centre of the Earth

A uniform gravitational field

In a relatively small region, for instance across a soccer pitch, across a small country, even up a high mountain, the Earth's gravitational field lines are almost parallel.

Figure 4.4b shows the small shaded section of the Earth's field from Figure 4.4a. The distance apart of the field lines is effectively constant, and the gravitational field strength also varies little in this comparatively small region. So you can consider the Earth's gravitational field within a small region to be uniform. This simplifies calculations.

Work done in a uniform gravitational field

The weight of a kilogram is 9.8 N on the Earth's surface. If you raise it 1.0 m,

$$\text{work} = \text{force} \times \text{distance} = 9.8 \text{ N} \times 1.0 \text{ m} = 9.8 \text{ J}$$

If you raise it 1.0 m its potential energy (PE) increases by 9.8 J. (Strictly, the mass itself does not have PE. The PE is a property of both the mass and the Earth, which pull each other together.)

To raise a mass of 1 kg through 2 m needs 9.8 N $\times$ 2 m = 19.6 J, and its PE increases by 19.6 J during this process.

For a mass m, in a gravitational field g, the force needed to raise it is mg. If you raise it through a height Δh, then

$$\text{increase in PE} = \text{work done} = \text{force} \times \text{distance} = mg \times \Delta h = mg\Delta h$$

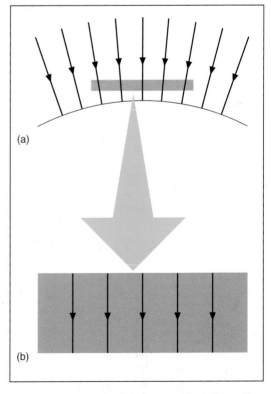

Figure 4.4 Across a relatively small region, the Earth's field is effectively uniform

Gravitational potential

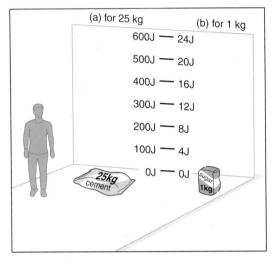

Figure 5.1 It takes 400 J to raise 25 kg to the height of the man, and 16 J to raise a kilogram to the same height

Gravitational potential difference

You can mark a wall to show the potential energy differences for a particular mass. Figure 5.1a shows the marks for a mass of 25 kg, the mass of a small bag of cement. They show the energy needed to raise that bag different heights. But the marks are not very helpful for a different mass.

More useful are the values of the potential energy differences for each kilogram. The **gravitational potential difference** between two points is the potential energy difference per kilogram. You might like to compare gravitational potential difference with electrical potential difference, which you studied in Chapter 29 of *Mechanics and Electricity*. Gravitational p.d. is energy difference per kilogram; electrical p.d. is energy difference per coulomb.

Figure 5.1b shows potential difference marks drawn at 4 J kg^{-1} intervals up a wall. At the Earth's surface, these marks are 0.41 m apart:

$$4 \text{ J} = 1 \text{ kg} \times 9.8 \text{ N kg}^{-1} \times 0.41 \text{ m}$$

But as you get higher, the gravitational field strength decreases. So the 4 J kg^{-1} marks get further apart.

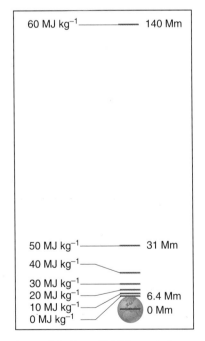

Figure 5.2 About 60 MJ is needed to take each kilogram a third of the way to the Moon

Getting free of the Earth

Figure 5.2 shows energy lines 10 MJ apart for a 1 kg mass. The first 10 MJ takes a 1 kg mass up the first 1.2 Mm; the next 10 MJ takes it 1.8 Mm higher; the next takes it 2.9 Mm higher; and 60 MJ is enough to take a 1 kg mass from the Earth's surface to a height of 140 Mm, more than a third of the way to the Moon.

At this distance, the gravitational field is so small that it takes very little energy to move each extra metre away from the Earth. Indeed, another 3 MJ is enough energy to get 1 kg to an infinite distance – completely free from the Earth. Each kilogram at the Earth's surface needs 63 MJ to get it completely free from the Earth's gravity.

Gravitational potential

The gravitational **potential at a point** is the potential energy of a kilogram at that point, compared with its potential energy an infinite distance away. Each kilogram on the Earth's surface has less potential energy than it would have if it were an infinite distance from the Earth. It has 63 MJ less, so the potential at the Earth's surface is −63 MJ kg^{-1} as Figure 5.3a shows. The potential 12.2 Mm from the centre of the Earth is −33 MJ kg^{-1}. This means that each kilogram has 33 MJ less potential energy than it would have at infinity. It needs 33 MJ to move from 12 Mm to infinity.

The potential V at a distance r from a mass M is given by the formula

$$V = -GM/r$$

Figure 5.3b shows a graph of potential against distance for the Earth's gravitational field. The graph is a hyperbola ($y \propto 1/x$) since $V \propto 1/r$.

The Sun has a mass of 2.0×10^{30} kg. The Earth is 1.5×10^{11} m from the Sun. The gravitational potential due to the Sun at this distance from the Sun is

$$V = -GM/r$$

$$= -6.7 \times 10^{-11} \text{ N m}^2 \text{ kg}^{-2} \times 2.0 \times 10^{30} \text{ kg}/(1.5 \times 10^{11} \text{ m})$$

$$= -890 \text{ MJ kg}^{-1}$$

At the distance of the Earth's orbit, it would take 890 MJ to move each kilogram to infinity, completely free from the Sun's gravitational attraction. Compare this with the 63 MJ kg^{-1} to get free from the Earth. Starting from the Earth, it needs more than ten times as much energy to get free from the Sun than from the Earth. To travel to the Moon, you need to get free from the Earth, but you stay the same distance from the Sun. But to travel to the outer planets you need to get free of the Sun as well, which needs much more energy.

Escape speed

If you throw a mass upwards, giving it 9.8 J kg^{-1} of kinetic energy, it has enough energy to rise a metre away from the Earth. If you give it 10 MJ kg^{-1}, it can rise to a height of 1.2 Mm. If you give the mass 63 MJ kg^{-1} of kinetic energy, an amount equal to its potential shortage at the Earth's surface, it has enough kinetic energy to become completely free of the Earth's surface. Such an object is travelling at its **escape speed**; it is travelling fast enough to leave the Earth's gravitational field.

At the escape speed, kinetic energy per kilogram = gravitational potential needed to get free:

$$\tfrac{1}{2} mv^2/m = GM/r \quad \text{or} \quad \tfrac{1}{2}v^2 = GM/r$$

so $\quad v = \sqrt{(2GM/r)}$

On the Earth's surface the escape speed is

$$\sqrt{(2GM/r)} = \sqrt{[2 \times 6.7 \times 10^{-11} \text{ N m}^2 \text{ kg}^{-2} \times 6.0 \times 10^{24} \text{ kg}/(6.4 \times 10^6 \text{ m})]}$$

$$= 11.2 \text{ km s}^{-1}$$

This is about 33 times the speed of sound in air.

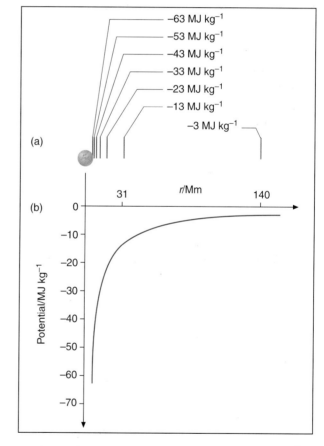

(a)

(b)

Figure 5.3 *The potential at the Earth's surface is –63 MJ kg^{-1}*

6 Coulomb's law

Measuring charge

- Rub a polythene strip with a duster to charge it negatively. Then scrape some of that charge onto the top cap of a coulombmeter to measure the charge (Figure 6.1).
- Repeat the experiment using an acetate rod rubbed to charge it positively.
- Connect together the terminals of a charged coulombmeter with a piece of wire; note what happens.
- Repeat with a piece of paper. Then try pieces of a range of materials.

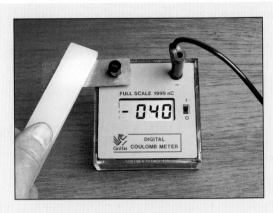

Figure 6.1 Charging a coulombmeter

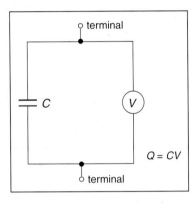

Figure 6.2 The charge Q = CV

The coulombmeter

You learnt in Chapter 9 of *Mechanics and Electricity* about two types of charge: positive and negative. You can measure charge with a coulombmeter.

Figure 6.2 shows the circuit of a coulombmeter. It is a voltmeter connected across a known capacitance. The meter is calibrated to indicate the charge Q: the capacitance C multiplied by the voltage V.

Electrons will move through a conductor placed between the terminals of a coulombmeter and discharge the capacitor. But electrons cannot move through an insulator. So if an insulator is placed between the terminals of a coulombmeter, the coulombmeter will not be discharged.

Electrons and protons

You learnt in Chapter 27 of *Matter and Waves* that a negatively charged object has more electrons than protons. A positively charged object has more protons than electrons. The size of the charge on a proton is the same as the size of the charge on an electron. This is called the electronic charge. It is negative on an electron (-1.6×10^{-19} C) and positive on a proton ($+1.6 \times 10^{-19}$ C). An object can only have a whole number of protons or electrons. So its charge must be a multiple of 1.6×10^{-19} C.

Figure 6.3 Measure the force between the two polythene rods

Forces between charges

- Place a charged polythene rod on an insulator resting on the pan of a sensitive balance and hold another charged rod near it (Figure 6.3).
- How does the direction of the force depend on the sign of the charge?
- Investigate how the size of the force depends on the distance between the charges.

Coulomb's law

The force between two charges obeys a law similar to that between two masses. The force is larger if the charges are large, and if the charges are close together. For the two point charges q and Q, separated by a distance r in Figure 6.4, the force between them is

$$F = kqQ/r^2$$

where k has the value 9.0×10^9 N m^2 C^{-2} in a vacuum or air. This formula is known as **Coulomb's law**.

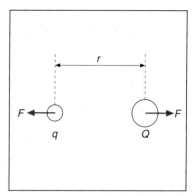

Figure 6.4 There are forces between pairs of charges

Positive and negative forces

All gravitational forces are attractive, but electrostatics forces can be either attractive or repulsive (Figure 6.5).

If both charges are positive, the formula for Coulomb's law $F = kqQ/r^2$ gives a positive value, and the force is repulsive. With two negative charges, the formula again gives a positive value, and the force is again repulsive.

With one positive charge and one negative charge, the formula gives a negative value, showing that the force is attractive.

You can use Coulomb's law to calculate the force between two spherical charges. If you charge a small conducting ball with a 5000 V power supply, it acquires a charge of about 12 nC. If two of these spheres are placed with their centres 6.0 cm apart, the force between them is

$$F = kqQ/r^2$$

$$= 9.0 \times 10^9 \text{ N m}^2 \text{ C}^{-2} \times 12 \times 10^{-9} \text{ C} \times 12 \times 10^{-9} \text{ C}/(0.06 \text{ m})^2$$

$$= 0.36 \text{ mN}$$

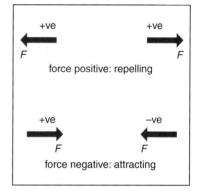

Figure 6.5 Like charges repel: the force is positive. Unlike charges attract: the force is negative

This force is small, about a hundredth of the weight of a page of this book. But this force is measurable. Electrostatic forces between small bodies are noticeable, unlike gravitational forces between small bodies.

The constant k depends on the material between the charges. It has the value 9.0×10^9 N m^2 C^{-2} in vacuum or air. Its value is calculated from the formula

$$k = 1/(4\pi\varepsilon_0)$$

where ε_0 is the permittivity of a vacuum; ε_0 has the value 8.85×10^{-12} F m^{-1}. You will learn more about ε_0 in Chapter 9.

Circular motion under electrostatic forces

A body can perform circular motion under electrostatic forces. Chapter 29 of *Matter and Waves* discussed one model of the hydrogen atom, which considers it to be an electron orbiting a proton (Figure 6.6).

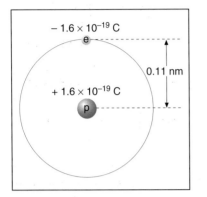

Figure 6.6 *A model of a hydrogen atom*

The electrostatic attraction of the proton on the electron provides the centripetal force for the electron's motion, so

centripetal force = electrostatic force:

$$mv^2/r = kqQ/r^2 \qquad \text{or} \qquad mv^2 = kqQ/r$$

so $v^2 = kqQ/mr$

For an electron orbiting a proton, the mass m of the electron is 9.1×10^{-31} kg, and the charges q and Q are $\pm1.6 \times 10^{-19}$ C. If the distance between their centres is approximately 0.11 nm, then

$$v = \sqrt{(kqQ/mr)}$$

$$= \sqrt{\left(\frac{9.0 \times 10^9 \text{ N m}^2 \text{ C}^{-2} \times (1.6 \times 10^{-19} \text{ C})^2}{9.1 \times 10^{-31} \text{ kg} \times 0.11 \times 10^{-9} \text{ m}} \right)}$$

$$= 1.6 \times 10^6 \text{ m s}^{-1}$$

Electric fields

Electric field strength

An **electric field** is a region in which there are forces on charges. As you would expect, the fields themselves are caused by charges. The **electric field strength** at a point is the force exerted by an electric field on one coulomb:

electric field strength = force/charge   or $E = F/q$

The unit of electric field strength is the newton per coulomb ($N\ C^{-1}$).

If a charge q is a distance r from another charge Q, you know from the last chapter that the force F between them is given by the formula

$$F = kqQ/r^2$$

The charge Q has an electric field strength

$$E = F/q = (kqQ/r^2)/q = kQ/r^2$$

This formula allows you to calculate the field strength at any distance from a charge.

At a distance of 0.1 m from the centre of the charge of 20 nC in Figure 7.1,

$$E = kQ/r^2$$

$$= 9.0 \times 10^9\ N\ m^2\ C^{-2} \times 20 \times 10^{-9}\ C/(0.1\ m)^2 = 18\ kN\ C^{-1}$$

Twice as far away from the centre of the charge, the field strength is $4.5\ kN\ C^{-1}$. The electric field strength of a point charge obeys the inverse square law: if you double the distance from the charge, you quarter the field strength. Figure 7.2 is a graph of field strength against distance from Q.

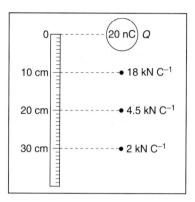

Figure 7.1 The field strength decreases as you get further from charge Q

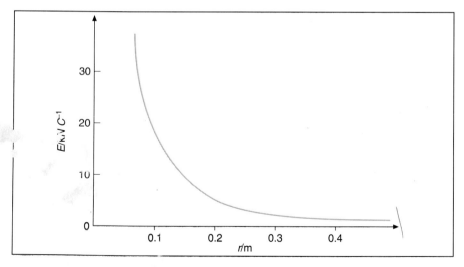

Figure 7.2 Field strength obeys an inverse square law with distance

Finding the shape of electric fields

- Connect a 5000 V power supply to two straight electrodes immersed in castor oil, as shown in Figure 7.3. Then sprinkle semolina grains on to the castor oil. Draw the pattern that results.
- Repeat for the point and circular electrodes shown in Figure 7.4

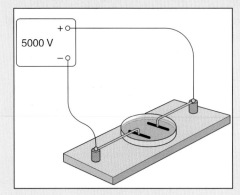

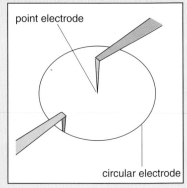

Figure 7.3 *The power supply sets up an electric field between the plates*

Figure 7.4 *These electrodes set up a radial field*

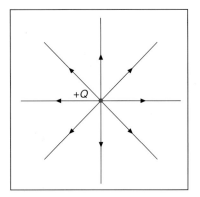

Figure 7.5 *The field of a point charge is radial*

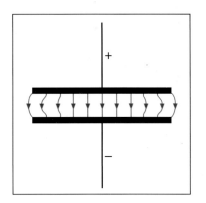

Figure 7.6 *The field is uniform where the field lines are parallel*

The field around a point charge

If you put a positive charge q anywhere near another positive charge Q, the force on q is always directed away from Q. The lines on Figure 7.5 are field lines. They show the directions of the electric force at any point due to charge Q. The field lines are radial. They are all directed out from the centre of charge.

Near Q, where the lines are close together, the field is stronger. A long way from Q, where the field lines are further apart, the field is weaker.

If Q is negative, the field lines are directed towards the charge. The field is radial, but inwards.

A uniform electric field

In the middle of the region between two parallel plates, the electric field lines are parallel (Figure 7.6). The lines are a constant distance apart; the electric field strength varies little in this region. This is a uniform field.

Work done in an electric field

Figure 7.7 shows a charge q between two parallel plates. When the charge moves from one plate to the other, the work done = force × distance = Fx.

The energy of the system changes as the charge moves from one plate to the other. You know from Chapter 29 of *Mechanics and Electricity* that change in energy = charge × potential difference. When the charge q in Figure 7.7 moves from one plate to the other, the change in energy is qV.

Electron guns

An electric field will push positive charges along the field lines from positive to negative. As the field pushes the charge, potential energy decreases. If the charge is unrestrained, its kinetic energy increases by the same amount. If the charge is negative, the same thing happens except that the charge moves in the opposite direction from negative to positive.

In the **electron gun** shown in Figure 7.8, the low-voltage supply powers the heater, which heats the cathode. When the cathode gets hot, its atoms vibrate more vigorously, throwing off some of the electrons. This is called **thermionic emission**. The high-voltage power supply attracts electrons from the cathode to the anode. Some pass through the hole in the anode and produce an electron beam. The beam produces a visible spot when it hits the fluorescent screen.

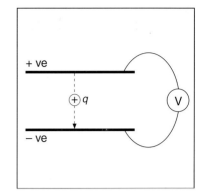

Figure 7.7 When charge moves between the plates, work done = qV

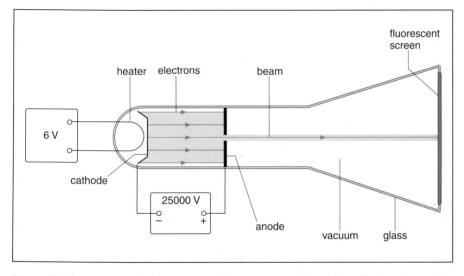

Figure 7.8 Electrons gain kinetic energy as they are attracted from the cathode to the anode

The potential energy lost as the electrons go from the cathode to the anode is equal to the kinetic energy gained:

$$qV = \tfrac{1}{2}mv^2$$

The charge and mass of an electron are $(-)1.6 \times 10^{-19}$ C and 9.1×10^{-31} kg respectively. In a computer monitor, the electrons typically are accelerated through 25 kV. So PE lost = KE gained:

$$qV = \tfrac{1}{2}mv^2 \qquad \text{so} \qquad v^2 = 2qV/m$$

$$\text{and} \quad v = \sqrt{(2qV/m)}$$

$$= \sqrt{[2 \times 1.6 \times 10^{-19} \text{ C} \times 25\,000 \text{ V}/(9.1 \times 10^{-31} \text{ kg})]}$$

$$\approx 9.3 \times 10^7 \text{ m s}^{-1}$$

8 Electrical potential

Equipotentials

- Connect a 2 V a.c. power supply to a pair of copper electrodes in copper sulphate solution. Use a digital voltmeter to check the voltage across the electrodes. Then put the probe in the copper sulphate solution and find places where the potential is 1 V (Figure 8.1).
- Sketch a diagram to mark the arrangement of these places. Repeat for voltages of 0.5 V and 1.5 V.
- Repeat for the point and circular electrodes (Figure 8.2).

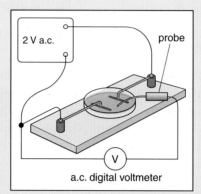

Figure 8.1 Find the places where the voltage is 1 V

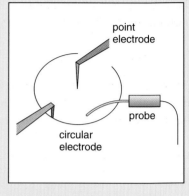

Figure 8.2 Investigate the voltages between the centre and the outside circle

Equipotential surfaces

Figure 8.3 shows two parallel plates at potentials (voltages) 0 V and 2 V. The lines between them show the potentials at places between these plates. As you would expect, the potential drops steadily from 2 V to 0 V across the gap between the plates. The lines of equal voltage on the diagram are **equipotentials**. In the uniform field between the two plates, the equipotentials are evenly spaced.

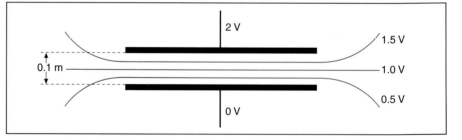

Figure 8.3 Equipotentials between two parallel plates

'Equipotential' means equal energy. (Strictly it means equal energy per unit charge, since potential is energy per unit charge.) If a charge moves along an equipotential, its energy does not change.

Compare Figure 8.3 with Figure 7.6, which shows the electric field lines between two parallel plates. You can see that the field lines are perpendicular to the equipotentials.

Potential gradient

Figure 8.4 shows a graph of potential against distance across the centre of the plates of Figure 8.3. The graph is a straight line: the potential drops uniformly with distance.

Figure 8.5 shows a potential–distance graph for two plates a distance x apart with a potential difference V between the plates. A positive charge between the two plates would be repelled from the positive plate and attracted to the negative plate. It moves down the potential gradient.

You know from the last chapter that, when a charge moves from one plate to another, the work done $= qV$. This is equal to force $\times$ distance $= Fx$. So

$$Fx = qV \qquad \text{or} \qquad F/q = V/x$$

F/q is the electric field strength, E. So $E = V/x$. V/x is the **potential gradient**. It is the electrical 'slope' of a field. In uniform fields, potential–distance graphs are straight lines. The potential gradient is constant and the electric field strength is constant. When the potential gradient is large, the electrical slope is large and the electric field strength is large, so there is a large force on charged particles.

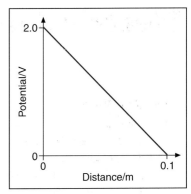

Figure 8.4 Potential–distance graph for Figure 8.3

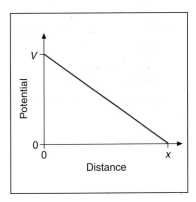

Figure 8.5 The electric field strength equals the potential gradient: $E = V/x$

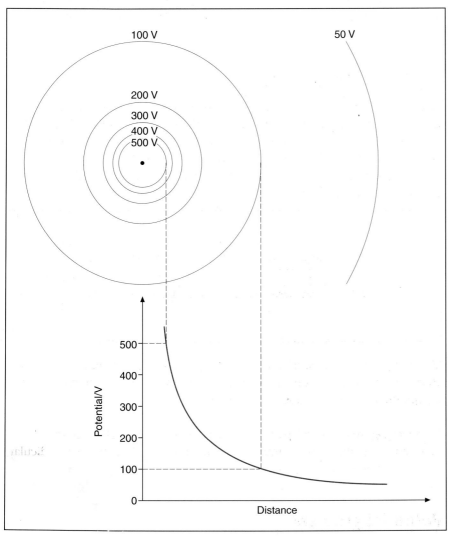

Figure 8.6 The further away you are from a point charge, the further apart are the equipotentials

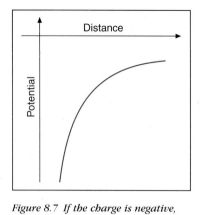

Figure 8.7 If the charge is negative, the potential is negative

Equipotentials for a radial field

Figure 8.6 shows the equipotentials for a radial field and a graph of potential against distance. The potential gets less the further you are from the charge, and the equipotentials get further apart. The electric field strength, the potential gradient, is weaker at a greater distance from the charge.

You can calculate the potential V at a distance from a charge Q from the formula

$$V = kQ/r$$

where $k = 1/(4\pi\varepsilon_0) = 9.0 \times 10^9$ N m^2 C^{-2} in vacuum or air.

Figure 8.7 shows how potential varies with distance from a negative charge. Compare this with Figure 5.3, which shows how potential varies with distance from a mass. The (gravitational) potential at a point is the energy per kilogram at a point compared with the energy at infinity; the electrical potential at a point is the energy per coulomb at a point compared with the energy at infinity.

Table 8.1 makes some comparisons between gravitational and electric fields.

Table 8.1 *Gravitational and electric fields compared*

Gravitational field	Electric field
mass	charge
force per unit mass	force per unit charge
N kg^{-1}	N C^{-1}
field strength is proportional to mass	field strength is proportional to charge
field obeys inverse square law	field obeys inverse square law
gravitational fields result in attraction only	with electric fields you can have repulsion and attraction

Worked example

Calculate the energy needed to remove an electron from a hydrogen atom.
At the end of Chapter 6 it was assumed that the electron in a hydrogen atom is 0.11 nm from the proton. The potential at this point is

$$kQ/r = 9 \times 10^9 \text{ N m}^2 \text{ C}^{-2} \times 1.6 \times 10^{-19} \text{ C}/(0.11 \times 10^{-9} \text{ m}) = 13 \text{ V}$$

If you remove an electron from a hydrogen atom, it moves through a potential difference of 13 V. The work done = charge × voltage = 13 eV.
This calculation is an approximation; it ignores the kinetic energy of the electron in the hydrogen atom. In Chapter 29 of *Matter and Waves*, you read that the ground-state electron in a hydrogen atom is in a potential well of 13.6 eV.

9 Charging capacitors

Charging and discharging a capacitor

- In the circuit in Figure 9.1, connect the free lead to point A. Measure and record the current every 10 s until it drops to a negligible value. Move the lead to point B and repeat.
- Plot graphs to show how the charging and discharging currents vary with time.
- Repeat the experiment, but this time use a resistance of 40 kΩ in the circuit.
- Repeat the experiment again; this time use a resistance

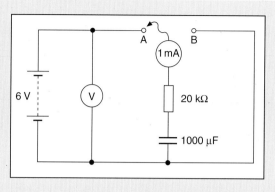

Figure 9.1 *Charge the capacitor and then discharge it*

Time constant

In Chapter 37 of *Mechanics and Electricity* you learnt about charging capacitors at different rates. Both charging and discharging are exponential processes, like radioactive decay. It does not matter how long you observe, the process goes on indefinitely. The current never drops completely to zero.

But it is still possible to define a time related to the charging or discharging graph. This is called the **time constant**. The time constant is the time for the current to decrease to 1/e of its original value. The number e is approximately 2.718. So the time constant is the time for the current to decrease to 1/2.718 of its original value. Figure 9.2 shows the charging graph for the circuit of Figure 9.1. The time constant is 20 s. During this time the current drops from 300 μA to (300 μA)/e = 110 μA.

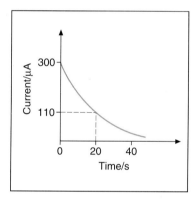

Figure 9.2 *The time constant of this discharge is 20 s*

The time constant for charging or discharging depends on the resistance and the capacitance. If you increase the resistance, the initial charging current is reduced, and the charging process takes longer. If you increase the capacitance, the amount of charge needed to charge it fully increases and, other things being equal, charging therefore takes longer. So

$$\text{time constant} = \text{resistance} \times \text{capacitance}$$
$$= RC$$

Figure 9.3 shows how the charging current varies for a circuit of time constant RC.

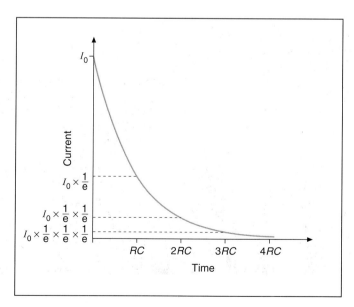

Figure 9.3 *After every interval RC, the current drops by a factor 1/e*

21

CHARGING CAPACITORS

The unit of resistance is the ohm, Ω (volt per amp; see Chapter 32 of *Mechanics and Electricity*), and the unit of capacitance is the farad, F (coulomb per volt; see Chapter 38 of *Mechanics and Electricity*). So the unit of time constant is $\Omega \times F = (V/A) \times (C/V) = (V/A) \times (A\,s/V) = s$. So, as you might expect, the unit of time constant is the second.

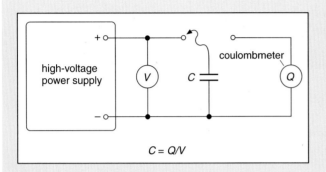

$$C = Q/V$$

Figure 9.4 Measuring a small capacitance

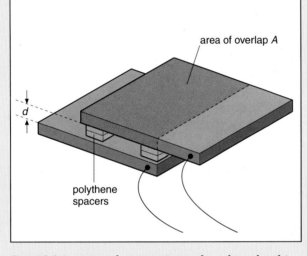

Figure 9.5 Investigate how capacitance depends on d and A

Measuring capacitance with a coulombmeter

- It is difficult to measure the charge stored in a small capacitance by plotting a current–time graph, because the time constant is small, and the charging process happens too quickly. But you can use a coulombmeter to measure the charge stored.
- Set up the circuit in Figure 9.4, using a capacitor made from two parallel metal plates, as shown in Figure 9.5.
- Measure the power supply voltage. Then charge the capacitor from the power supply. Discharge the capacitor into the coulombmeter and measure the charge stored. Divide the charge by the voltage to find the capacitance.
- Vary the area of overlap A (Figure 9.5) and investigate how capacitance depends on A. Then vary the separation d of the plates and investigate how capacitance depends on d.
- Compare the capacitance of an air-spaced capacitor with that of a capacitor filled with polythene (polyethene).

The parallel-plate capacitor

The capacitance C of a parallel-plate capacitor depends on the area A of the plates, their separation d, and the medium between the plates:

$$C = \varepsilon_0 \varepsilon_r A/d$$

You met ε_0 in Coulomb's law in Chapter 6. It is the permittivity of a vacuum, and its value is 8.85×10^{-12} F m^{-1}. The symbol ε_r represents the relative permittivity. It is a constant that depends on the medium between the plates of a capacitor. The relative permittivities of air and vacuum are both 1. But the relative permittivities of other insulators are greater than 1. If you replace the air between the plates of a capacitor with polythene, whose relative permittivity is 2.2, the capacitance will be 2.2 times bigger. You can read on page 55 why this happens.

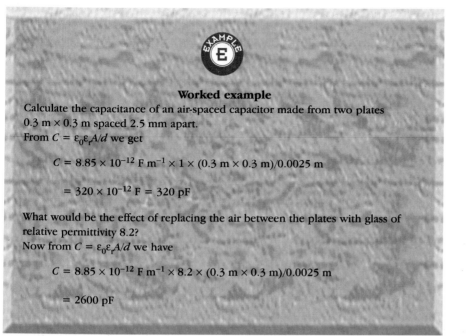

Worked example

Calculate the capacitance of an air-spaced capacitor made from two plates 0.3 m × 0.3 m spaced 2.5 mm apart.

From $C = \varepsilon_0\varepsilon_r A/d$ we get

$$C = 8.85 \times 10^{-12} \text{ F m}^{-1} \times 1 \times (0.3 \text{ m} \times 0.3 \text{ m})/0.0025 \text{ m}$$

$$= 320 \times 10^{-12} \text{ F} = 320 \text{ pF}$$

What would be the effect of replacing the air between the plates with glass of relative permittivity 8.2?

Now from $C = \varepsilon_0\varepsilon_r A/d$ we have

$$C = 8.85 \times 10^{-12} \text{ F m}^{-1} \times 8.2 \times (0.3 \text{ m} \times 0.3 \text{ m})/0.0025 \text{ m}$$

$$= 2600 \text{ pF}$$

Making small capacitors

Miniature electronic devices need large values of capacitance in as small a space as possible. So capacitors are built with very small plate spacing, very thin plates and with insulators of high relative permittivity. They are often rolled up to save space. Figure 9.6 shows a polystyrene capacitor and a diagram of its construction.

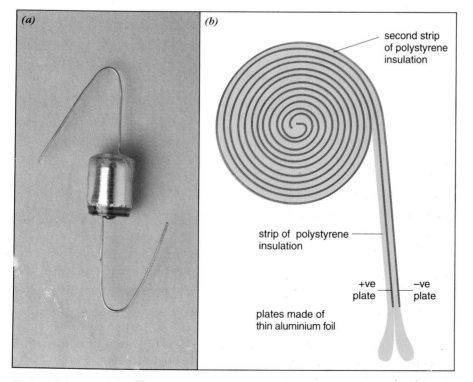

(a)

(b)

second strip
of polystyrene
insulation

strip of polystyrene
insulation

+ve
plate

−ve
plate

plates made of
thin aluminium foil

Figure 9.6 (a) A polystyrene capacitor.

(b) You need thin plates and thin dielectrics to keep the physical size of capacitors small

Magnets

Bar magnets

- Place a bar magnet on a cork floating in water. Compare its final orientation with that of a compass needle placed 1 m away.
- What happens as you bring the compass needle nearer and nearer to the floating magnet?
- Hold a bar magnet in each hand. Feel the force exerted as you slowly bring the ends of the magnets together. Reverse one magnet and repeat. What happens if you now reverse the other magnet?

Figure 10.1 Suspended magnets align north–south

Magnetic fields

Any freely suspended bar magnet will rotate until it points in a north–south direction, as shown in Figure 10.1.

The end of the bar magnet pointing towards the Earth's magnetic North Pole is referred to as its north-seeking pole or, more simply, its north pole. The other end is its south-seeking, or south, pole.

As the north poles of two bar magnets are brought together, they repel. The same thing happens with two south poles. A north and a south pole attract.

A force acts between the poles before they are touching. This force increases as the poles get closer together. Around a bar magnet there is a **magnetic field**, a region within which there are magnetic forces.

A suspended magnet aligns with the Earth's magnetic field unless there is a stronger magnetic field present. Two compass needles held close together affect each other, so that neither points towards magnetic north.

Magnetic field patterns

- Support a piece of stiff card above a bar magnet. Sprinkle some iron filings onto the card and tap it gently. Sketch the observed pattern.
- Investigate the field between two magnets, first with opposite poles facing and then with like poles facing.
- Place a bar magnet in the centre of a sheet of white paper, trace its outline and put a cross close to its north pole. Place a small plotting compass so that the south end of its needle is above the cross. Mark the position of the north end of the needle. Continue to move the plotting compass, marking the position of its north end (Figure 10.2).
- Repeat this procedure for various starting points around the magnet.

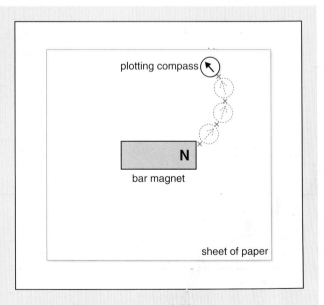

Figure 10.2 Plotting a magnetic field pattern

Magnetic field lines

Iron filings show the shape of a magnetic field by aligning themselves with the magnetic field lines. The north end of the needle of a plotting compass indicates the direction of a magnetic field. Magnetic field lines leave the north pole of a magnet and enter at its south pole, as shown in Figure 10.3. The field lines are closest together at the poles where the magnetic field is strongest.

The magnetic field lines between two attracting poles go from one pole to the other, seeming to pull the magnets together. Those between two like poles do not combine, as the poles push each other apart (Figure 10.4). A **neutral point** exists between the two repelling magnets where their magnetic fields cancel.

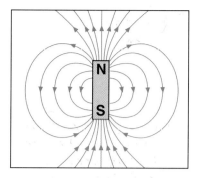

Figure 10.3 Magnetic field of a bar magnet

Breaking a bar magnet

- Use a plotting compass to check that a thin steel rod has both a north and a south pole.
- Carefully break the rod in half and check the broken ends in the same way. Break the rod into smaller pieces and check their ends.
- Is it possible to produce a single magnetic pole in this way?

Magnetic domains

Whenever a magnet is broken in half, two smaller magnets, each having their own north and south poles, are produced. However small the resulting magnet, it always has a north and a south pole.

A long magnet appears to consist of a large number of smaller individual magnets that are all aligned in the same direction. Breaking a magnet simply produces smaller and smaller pieces with all their tiny individual magnets still aligned, as shown in Figure 10.5.

Magnetic materials behave as though they are made of many microscopic magnets. These microscopic magnets get their behaviour from the motion of their electrons. The microscopic magnets within a magnetic material consist of a group, or **domain**, of atoms with their own magnetic fields aligned. In a magnetised material, the fields of all the domains are aligned, as shown in Figure 10.6a. In an unmagnetised magnetic material, the fields of the domains are randomly orientated. Their magnetic effects cancel each other out, as shown in Figure 10.6b.

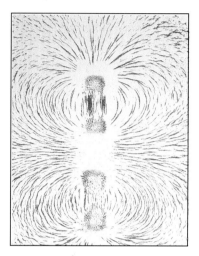

Figure 10.4 The two bar magnets beneath this card are repelling

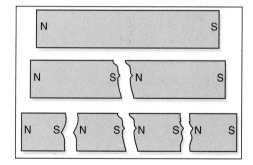

Figure 10.5 A magnet always has two poles

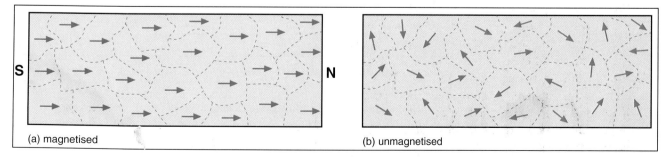

(a) magnetised

(b) unmagnetised

Figure 10.6 Orientation of magnetic domains in a magnetic material when it is (a) magnetised and (b) unmagnetised

Magnetic effects of currents

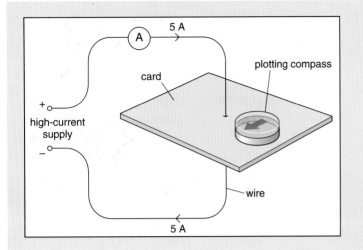

The magnetic field of a current-carrying wire

- Push a length of insulated copper wire vertically through the centre of a horizontal piece of card (Figure 11.1). Pass a current of 5 A through the wire, noting the direction of the current.
- Use iron filings and a plotting compass to investigate the magnetic field around the wire.

Figure 11.1 The space around a wire carrying a current contains a magnetic field

The corkscrew rule

Any moving charge produces a magnetic field. The magnetic field lines due to a current through a wire are circles centred on the wire. Figure 11.2a shows the magnetic field looking down the wire in the direction of the current flow; the cross at the centre of the diagram is the symbol for current flowing into the diagram; you can imagine it as the back end of a dart carrying current away from you. Figure 11.2b shows the field due to a current coming out of the diagram; you can imagine the dot at the centre as the point of a dart carrying current towards you.

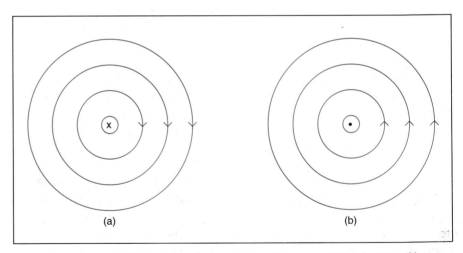

Figure 11.2 Magnetic field of a current flowing (a) into the page and (b) out of the page

A plotting compass shows that the field is clockwise when viewed along the direction of current flow. The corkscrew rule is a useful way of remembering this: a corkscrew has to be rotated clockwise to drive it forward into the cork of a wine bottle.

Magnetic fields of current-carrying rings and cylindrical coils

- Thread several turns of wire through two holes in a card to make a narrow coil with a diameter of 4 cm. Pass a current of 5 A through the coil (Figure 11.3a).
- Compare the current directions in the wire where it passes through the two holes in the card. Sketch the shape and direction of the magnetic field produced by this ring of current.
- Make a solenoid (a long coil) about 10 cm long with 20 turns of wire. Pass a current of 5 A through it (Figure 11.3b).
- Sketch the shape and direction of the magnetic field produced by the solenoid.

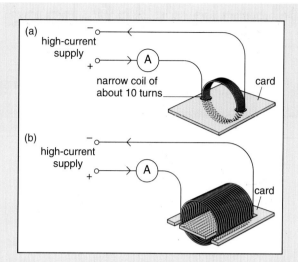

Figure 11.3 Current through coils

Magnetic fields associated with coils

The magnetic field associated with a current flowing in a coil is a resultant of all the magnetic fields produced around each part of each individual coil of wire.

Figure 11.4 shows a section through the magnetic field pattern for a single-turn coil. The current is shown flowing in on the left and out on the right. The magnetic field is clockwise on the left and anticlockwise on the right. Inside the coil, the magnetic fields are in the same direction and reinforce each other.

A solenoid is a cylindrical current-carrying coil of wire with a large number of turns. A section through its magnetic field pattern is shown in Figure 11.5. The magnetic field lines enter the solenoid at one end, leave at the other end, and loop around the outside to re-enter the solenoid at the same point. The field lines are continuous.

Through the centre of the solenoid, the magnetic fields produced by each of the current rings are all in the same direction, producing a larger resultant magnetic field along its axis. When a solenoid is long and narrow, the field lines through its centre are parallel and equally spaced, indicating that the magnetic field is uniform in this region.

Compare the magnetic field pattern of a solenoid (Figure 11.5) with that of a bar magnet (Figure 10.3). The shapes of the 'outside' fields are similar. Indeed, a common method of producing a bar magnet is to place a suitable length of steel inside a solenoid carrying a direct current. The field lines through the centre of the solenoid are like the aligned domains within the bar magnet.

The ends of a solenoid behave like the poles of a bar magnet, the north pole being the end where the field lines leave. Figure 11.6 shows a simple way of telling which solenoid pole you are facing from the direction of current flow.

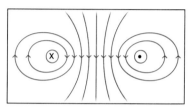

Figure 11.4 Resultant magnetic field of a narrow coil

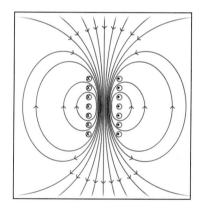

Figure 11.5 The magnetic field of a solenoid is like a bar magnet

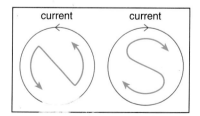

Figure 11.6 If you look at the end of a solenoid, the current direction shows which pole it is

12 Fleming's left-hand rule

Figure 12.1 Bar and magnadur magnets

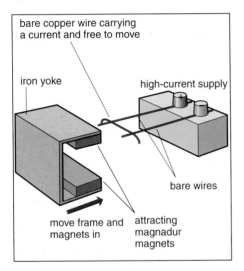

Figure 12.2 Position the attracting magnets above and below the wire

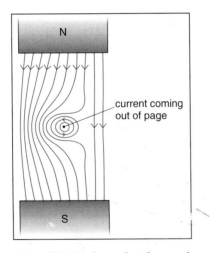

Figure 12.3 Resultant of uniform and circular magnetic fields

Magnadur magnets

Figure 12.1 shows two magnets with their north poles painted white. The bar magnet is long and thin with a pole at each end. The magnadur magnet is short and fat. Its poles are the large faces. A strong and uniform magnetic field is produced in the space between two attracting magnadur magnets held close together.

Magnetic catapult

- Place two attracting magnadur magnets on opposite sides of a soft-iron, U-shaped yoke. Use a plotting compass to find the direction of the magnetic field between them.
- Connect two parallel, horizontal lengths of stiff, bare wire to a power supply. Place a third length of bare wire across the other two, completing the circuit. Hold the yoke with the magnets above and below the wire (Figure 12.2) with their magnetic field acting downwards.
- What happens to the free wire when the power supply is turned on?
- Repeat with the magnetic field of the magnadurs acting upwards.
- What happens in each case if the current is reversed?

Catapult field

A wire carrying a current has its own magnetic field. When such a wire is in another field, the effect of the two fields is to produce a force on the wire. Figure 12.3 shows the magnetic field that is produced when a wire carries a current perpendicular to a uniform magnetic field.

To the right of the wire, the two magnetic fields are in the opposite direction and cancel out, while to its left they are in the same direction and reinforce. The resultant magnetic field is much stronger on the left, and the field lines get distorted around to this side of the wire. Think of the field lines as lengths of elastic, each one trying to return to the shortest possible length. It looks as though they are pushing the wire towards the right, and indeed there is a force on the wire in that direction.

The field due to the magnets is downwards; the current is out of the paper; the resulting force is to the right. All these three directions are at right angles to each other.

Fleming's left-hand rule (Figure 12.4) provides a way of remembering these directions, and can be used to predict the direction of one of these when the other two are known.

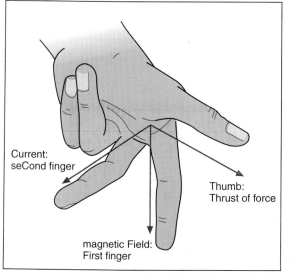

Figure 12.4 *Fleming's left-hand rule: when the First finger points in the direction of the magnetic Field and the seCond finger points in the direction of the Current, the Thumb gives the direction of the Thrust (or force) on the conductor*

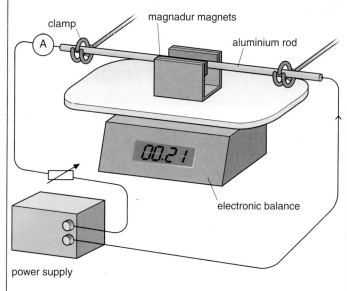

Figure 12.5 *The electronic balance measures the force produced by the interaction of the two magnetic fields*

Force on a current-carrying conductor in a magnetic field

- Set up the apparatus shown in Figure 12.5 as follows. Place the yoke with two attracting magnadurs on the balance. Zero the balance. Clamp an aluminium rod horizontally between the poles of the magnets. Pass a current of 1 A through the rod.
- Record the balance reading. What does a negative balance reading indicate? How could such a reading be made positive? Record a set of readings of current and force.
- Place another yoke of magnadurs on the balance to double the length of rod in the magnetic field. Make sure both fields are in the same direction. Record another set of current and force readings. Repeat using three yokes.
- On the same axes, plot a graph of force against current for each set of readings. What does your graph show?
- Observe the effect of a stronger magnetic field on the force by holding the magnadur magnets nearer to the rod.

How the force varies

The balance in Figure 12.5 registers the force exerted on the yoke: a force that is equal and opposite to that exerted on the clamped rod. A positive reading indicates that the yoke is being pushed down and that there is an upward force on the rod.

Increasing the magnetic field increases the force. The graphs in Figure 12.6 show that the force on a current-carrying wire in a magnetic field is proportional to the current.

For a given current, the force is directly proportional to the length of the current-carrying wire in the magnetic field. The graphs in Figure 12.6 are twice as steep when using twice the length, and three times as steep with three times the length.

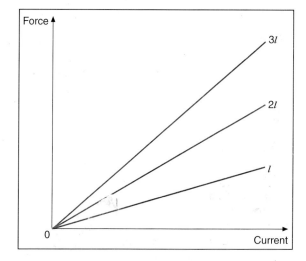

Figure 12.6 *Force exerted on different currents for different lengths of conductor*

Magnetic field strength

The tesla

In the last chapter, we saw that a conductor carrying a current I perpendicular to a magnetic field experiences a force F that is proportional to both the current flowing and the length l of conductor in the field. The force also depends on the strength of the magnetic field:

Table 13.1 *Typical values of magnetic flux density*

	Typical magnetic flux density/T
Earth	10^{-5}
air-cored solenoid	10^{-3}
magnadur magnet	10^{-1}
iron-cored solenoid	1

force = magnetic field strength × current × length

$$F = BIl$$

where B is the strength of the magnetic field called the **magnetic flux density**:

$$B = F/Il$$

So the SI unit of B is $N\ A^{-1}\ m^{-1}$. This is called the **tesla** (T). A magnetic flux density of 1 T produces a force of 1 N on each 1 m length of wire carrying a current of 1 A perpendicular to the field. Table 13.1 gives some typical values of magnetic flux density.

EXAMPLE

Worked example

Calculate the force exerted on 8 cm of wire when it carries a current of 2 A at right angles to a field of magnetic flux density 20 mT.
We get

$$F = BIl = 20 \times 10^{-3}\ T \times 2\ A \times 8 \times 10^{-2}\ m = 0.0032\ N = 3.2\ mN$$

Finding magnetic flux densities

- Repeat the experiment on page 29. Measure the force produced by a known current flowing perpendicularly to the field produced by a pair of attracting magnadurs. Measure the length of wire in the field. Calculate the magnetic flux density, $B = F/Il$, between the attracting magnadur magnets in the yoke.
- Insert a calibrated Hall probe (Figure 13.1) between the attracting magnadur magnets and compare its reading with your value measured directly from the force. Account for any differences.

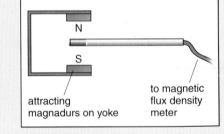

Figure 13.1 Using a Hall probe

The Hall probe

A **Hall probe** consists of a small, thin rectangle of semiconductor material. A constant current is passed through the length of the slice. When the probe is placed at right angles to a steady magnetic field, a voltage appears across the width of the slice. This Hall voltage, which is of the order of microvolts, is directly proportional to the flux density of the magnetic field. A sensitive digital voltmeter, connected across the slice, records the Hall voltage. Some Hall probes are pre-calibrated using known flux densities and give readings directly in teslas.

Measuring magnetic fields

- Insert a pre-calibrated Hall probe into the centre of a solenoid to measure the magnetic field strength there. Investigate how the field strength varies with the current flowing through the solenoid (Figure 13.2). Plot a graph of magnetic flux density against current.

- Connect three solenoids, with the same length and number of turns but different cross-sectional areas, in series. Pass a current of about 3 A through them. How does the magnetic flux density at the centre of a solenoid depend on its area?

- Two clamped half-metre rules (Figure 13.3) have 50 slinky turns between them. With the rules placed 20 cm apart, the number of turns per unit length is $50/(0.20\ \text{m}) = 250\ \text{m}^{-1}$. Record the flux density at the centre of this solenoid for a current of 8 A. Repeat using different numbers of turns per unit length. Plot a graph of magnetic flux density against number of turns per unit length.

- Use a Hall probe to measure the magnetic field strength 1 cm from a long straight wire carrying a current of 10 A (Figure 13.4). Repeat for a range of distances, and plot a graph of B against $1/r$.

- With r fixed at 1 cm, investigate how B depends on I.

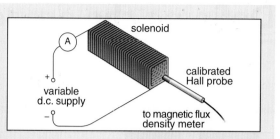

Figure 13.2 *The meter will read maximum when the field lines are perpendicular to the flat end of the probe*

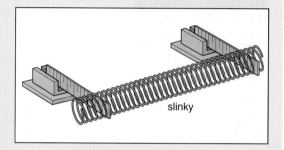

Figure 13.3 *Stretch the slinky to reduce the number of turns per unit length*

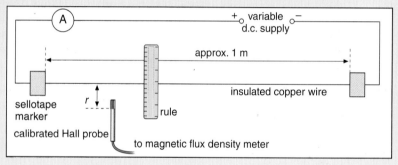

Figure 13.4 *Position the probe so that it is perpendicular to the circular magnetic field around the wire*

Permeability of free space

The magnetic field strength B within a solenoid is independent of the cross-sectional area of the solenoid, provided the length of the solenoid is large compared with its diameter. It depends on the current I flowing and on the number of turns per unit length, n (the turns density).

If the region inside a solenoid is air or a vacuum,

$$B = \mu_0 nI$$

where μ_0 is a constant called the permeability of free space and has the value $4\pi \times 10^{-7}\ \text{N A}^{-2}$.

For a long straight wire, B depends on the current I and the distance r from the wire:

$$B = \mu_0 I/2\pi r$$

Defining the ampere

Forces between parallel conductors

- Connect two lengths of thin aluminium foil so that they are close together and parallel (Figure 14.1). Allow sufficient slack so they can deflect but not touch.
- Observe what happens to the lengths of foil as you pass a current of about 5 A up one foil and down the other.
- Repeat the experiment, but this time change the connections so that the currents in both wires are flowing upwards. Then repeat with both currents flowing down.

Figure 14.1 Observe the two lengths of foil as the current is turned on

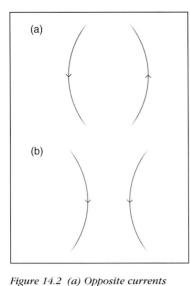

Figure 14.2 (a) Opposite currents repel but (b) parallel currents attract

Forces between currents

When the currents through the foils in Figure 14.1 are in opposite directions, they repel each other. The foils deflect apart when the current is first turned on. When the currents flow in the same direction through each foil, they attract. The foils deflect closer together when the current is first turned on. Figure 14.2 summarises these two observations.

Figure 14.3 shows two parallel conductors carrying opposite currents. A current I_1 flows down the conductor on the left. This produces a clockwise magnetic field B_1, which is perpendicular to the right-hand conductor. The current I_2, flowing up the right-hand conductor, flows at 90° to B_1. Applying Fleming's left-hand rule to the current I_2 shows that a force F acts on I_2 towards the right.

Similarly, the current I_2 through the right-hand conductor produces a field B_2 perpendicular to the left-hand conductor (Figure 14.4). Applying Fleming's left-hand rule to the current I_1 shows that it experiences a force to the left.

The forces on the two wires are equal and opposite. They form a Newton's third-law pair, which force the two current-carrying conductors apart.

Use similar reasoning to show why two parallel currents, flowing in the same direction, attract each other.

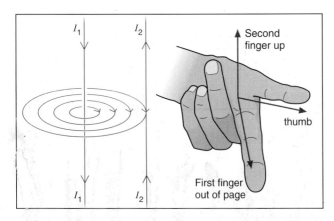

Figure 14.3 The current I_2 flows at 90° to the magnetic field B_1

Force equation

Using the equation $F = BIl$ for the two wires opposite gives

$$F_1 = B_2 I_1 l \qquad \text{and} \qquad F_2 = B_1 I_2 l$$

If the wires are distance r apart, we have $B = \mu_0 I/2\pi r$, so

$$F_1 = (\mu_0 I_2/2\pi r)I_1 l \qquad \text{and} \qquad F_2 = (\mu_0 I_1/2\pi r)I_2 l$$

Thus F_1 and F_2 have the same magnitude.
The force per unit length is

$$F/l = \mu_0 I_1 I_2/2\pi r$$

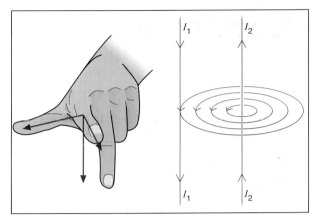

Figure 14.4 The current I_1 flows at 90° to the magnetic field B_2

The ampere

The above force equation defines the SI unit of electric current in terms of mechanical quantities: **One ampere** is that constant current which, when flowing through two infinitely long parallel straight conductors of negligible cross-section placed 1 m apart in a vacuum, produces a force per unit length between them of 2×10^{-7} N m^{-1}.

This definition of the ampere also determines the value of the permeability of free space, μ_0. From the definition, $I_1 = I_2 = 1$ A, $r = 1$ m and $F/l = 2 \times 10^{-7}$ N m^{-1}, so the equation for the force per unit length becomes

$$2 \times 10^{-7} \text{ N m}^{-1} = \mu_0 \times 1 \text{ A} \times 1 \text{ A}/(2\pi \times 1 \text{ m})$$

so $\quad \mu_0 = 2 \times 10^{-7}$ N m$^{-1} \times 2\pi \times 1$ m$/(1$ A $\times 1$ A$) = 4\pi \times 10^{-7}$ N A^{-2}

The electrostatic constant ε_0 depends on the electromagnetic constant μ_0. The permittivity and permeability of free space, ε_0 and μ_0, are connected by:

$$c = 1/\sqrt{(\varepsilon_0 \mu_0)}$$

where c is the speed of light; μ_0 is fixed by definition, so ε_0 is fixed by μ_0 and c.

The mains lead for an electric fire consists of two insulated, parallel copper wires whose centres are 2 mm apart. The fire operates at a current of 8 A. Calculate the force per unit length acting on the two wires, stating its direction.
We get

$$F/l = \mu_0 I_1 I_2/2\pi r$$

$$= 4\pi \times 10^{-7} \text{ N A}^{-2} \times 8 \text{ A} \times 8 \text{ A}/(2\pi \times 2 \times 10^{-3} \text{ m}) = 6.4 \times 10^{-3} \text{ N m}^{-1}$$

Current flows from the supply to the fire through one of the wires and returns to the supply through the other. The currents in the two wires flow in opposite directions. The force between the wires is repulsive.

Worked example

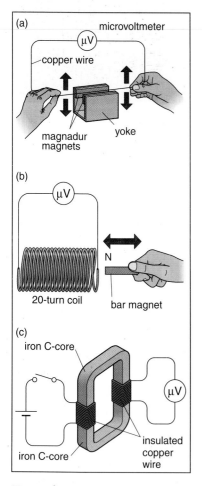

Figure 16.1 Moving conductors and magnetic fields

Moving conductors and magnetic fields

When there is a changing magnetic field in a circuit, or when a wire moves relative to a magnetic field, voltages are induced (generated). A voltage is induced when a conductor moves relative to a magnetic field (Figure 16.1a). Likewise, a voltage is induced when a magnetic field moves relative to a conductor (Figure 16.1b). Reversing the direction of motion of either induces a voltage in the opposite direction. A larger voltage results from faster movement, a stronger field and more turns. Figure 16.1c shows another way of moving a magnetic field relative to a conductor. What happens when the switch is closed and when it is opened?

Magnetic flux

You learnt in Chapter 13 that the strength of a magnetic field is called the magnetic flux density. This sounds as though it is to do with something flowing. You can imagine the magnetic field lines to be lines of **magnetic flux** or flow. Where the lines are closest, the flow density or flux density is greatest, and the field is strongest. With a bar magnet, the flux flows from north to south around the magnet. The flux flows in a circular path around a wire carrying a current.

The magnetic flux density B through an area is the amount of flux that passes through that area divided by the area (Figure 16.2):

$$\text{magnetic flux density} = (\text{magnetic flux})/\text{area}$$

so $$\text{magnetic flux} = \text{magnetic flux density} \times \text{area}$$

$$\Phi = BA$$

Here Φ, the Greek capital phi ('fi', rhymes with 'pie'), is the symbol for magnetic flux.

The SI unit of **magnetic flux** is the tesla metre squared ($T\,m^2$), called the weber (Wb). A tesla is equal to a weber per metre squared.

When a coil having N turns surrounds a magnetic flux Φ, each turn links a flux Φ. The total **magnetic flux link** the coil is $N\Phi$ (Figure 16.3).

Explaining the induced current

As a wire moves perpendicularly through a magnetic field, conduction electrons within the wire move with the wire and can be regarded as a current flowing through the field. The electrons experience a force acting at 90° to both field and direction of motion.

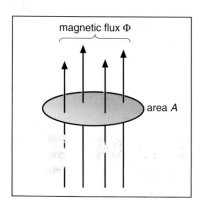

Figure 16.2 The flux density B = Φ/A

You can apply Fleming's left-hand rule to these conduction electrons (Figure 16.4). Remember that electrons moving to the right form a conventional current moving to the left. The electrons are forced towards end Y of the wire, which becomes negatively charged. End X becomes positively charged. A voltage or e.m.f. is induced across the ends of the wire. If the wire forms part of a circuit, then an induced current flows.

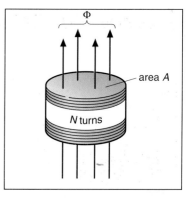

Figure 16.3 Magnetic flux linkage through coil is $N\Phi = NBA$

Faraday's law

Michael Faraday (1791–1867) discovered that the magnitude of an induced e.m.f. is directly proportional to the rate of change of magnetic flux linkage. So the induced e.m.f. $= N \, d\Phi/dt$. This is **Faraday's law**.

Direction of induced current and field

- Connect a cell, resistor and microvoltmeter to the coil (Figure 16.5a). Which way does the meter deflect? Use the polarity of the cell to determine the direction of current flow around the coil. Identify the north end of the coil.
- Remove the cell and resistor from the circuit (Figure 16.5b). Thrust the north pole of a bar magnet into what was the north end of the coil. Which way does the meter now deflect? What happens when the magnet is withdrawn?

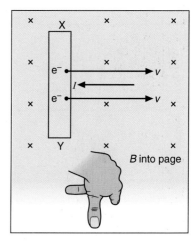

Figure 16.4 Apply Fleming's left-hand rule to the conduction electrons

Lenz's law

If you move the north pole of a magnet towards a loop of wire, it induces a current in that loop. The direction of the current makes the end of the loop facing the magnet itself acquire a north polarity, which repels the north pole of the magnet back. If the north pole moves away from the loop, this results in the facing end of the coil acquiring a south polarity, which pulls the north pole back, opposing the removal of the magnet from the coil.

This situation is an example of **Lenz's law**, which states that any current driven by an induced e.m.f. opposes the change causing it.

Faraday's law of electromagnetic induction is often written as

$$\text{induced e.m.f.} = -N \, d\Phi/dt$$

The negative sign indicates that the induced e.m.f. would produce a current that opposes the change causing it.

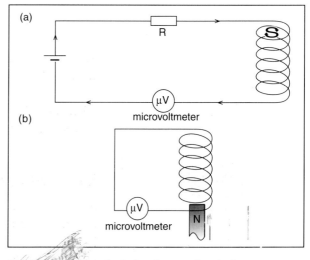

Figure 16.5 Finding the induced magnetic polarity

Applications of electromagnetic induction

Bar magnet falling through coil

- Connect a horizontal 300-turn coil to a voltage data-logger. Set the sample frequency to 500 Hz. Start the data-logger and immediately release the bar magnet (Figure 17.1).
- Use the recorded data values to plot a graph of induced e.m.f. against time. Explain the shape of the graph.
- Repeat the experiment, first reversing the magnet, and then dropping it from a greater height.

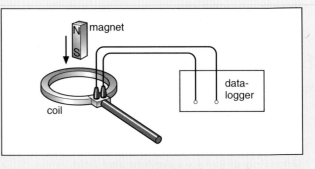

Figure 17.1 The data-logger samples the induced e.m.f. every 2 ms

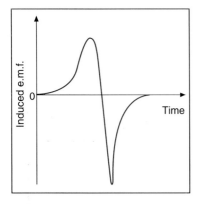

Figure 17.2 The e.m.f. induced across the coil

Changing magnetic flux linkage

If you drop a bar magnet through a coil, the flux through the coil increases as the bar magnet enters and decreases as it leaves. An e.m.f. is induced across the coil as the magnetic flux through it changes. The magnet is accelerating under gravity: it leaves the coil slightly faster than it enters. As Figure 17.2 shows, the maximum induced e.m.f. is greater as the magnet exits, although this e.m.f. is induced for a shorter time. If the magnet were dropped from a greater height, the e.m.f.s induced would be greater, because the rates of change of flux on entering and leaving would be greater. But the e.m.f.s would last for a shorter time, because the magnet is travelling faster.

If the terminals of the coil are connected together, instead of to the data-logger, an induced current flows through the coil when the magnet is dropped. The top of the coil becomes a south pole as the south pole of the magnet approaches (its entry is opposed). The bottom of the coil becomes a south pole as the magnet's north pole recedes (its exit is opposed).

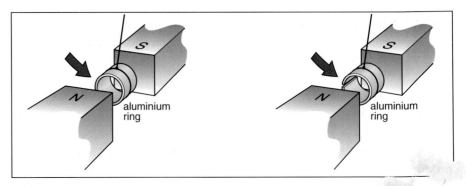

Figure 17.3 Induced currents in the complete ring oppose its motion

Figure 17.3 shows a situation where induced currents have very marked effects. Two aluminium rings are swinging between the poles of a magnet. The ring with a slit keeps swinging for a long time. The complete ring stops quickly. In both rings, a voltage is induced when they swing through the magnetic field. But in the complete ring a current can flow, which opposes the change producing it – the swinging of the ring through the field.

Cutting magnetic fields

Figure 17.4 shows a conductor of length l moving at speed v at 90° to a magnetic field B. In 1 s, the conductor moves a distance v, passing through an area lv of magnetic field. We have

> induced e.m.f. $= -N\, d\Phi/dt$

Since $\Phi = BA$ and the magnetic field is constant, this becomes

> e.m.f. $= -NB\, dA/dt$

Here there is a single piece of wire, so $N = 1$. Also $dA/dt = lv$. So

> e.m.f. $= -Blv$

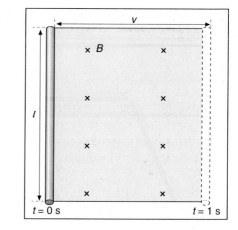

Figure 17.4 For conductor of length l moving at speed v, dA/dt = lv

The Earth's magnetic field

The Earth's magnetic field slopes, so has a horizontal and a vertical component. If you move a wire vertically, it cuts the horizontal component of the Earth's magnetic field. If you move a wire horizontally, it cuts the vertical component of the Earth's field.

Cutting the Earth's magnetic field

- This outdoor experiment requires you to work in a large group. Arrange 100 m of insulated wire into a square of side 25 m. Connect a sensitive voltmeter to the mid-point of the northern side (Figure 17.5).
- Hold the length AB, and quickly jump up with it from ground level to full stretch. Record the time taken to raise the wire and the reading on the voltmeter as you do so. Estimate the distance through which the wire was raised. Calculate its average speed.
- Hold the length AB at a constant height and run with it towards the meter. Record the voltmeter reading and the time taken to cover the distance of 25 m. Calculate the average speed.
- Calculate the horizontal and vertical components of the Earth's magnetic field. Combine these to obtain the Earth's resultant magnetic field.

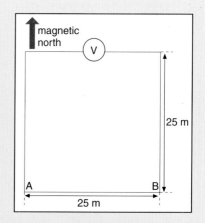

Figure 17.5 Digital voltmeter measures induced e.m.f.

Angle of dip

Figure 17.6 shows the horizontal and vertical components of the Earth's magnetic field in Britain. Their resultant is at an angle of about 70° to the horizontal. This is known as the angle of dip.

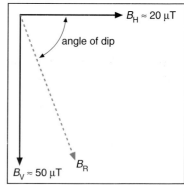

Figure 17.6 In Britain, the angle of dip is about 70°

Motors and generators

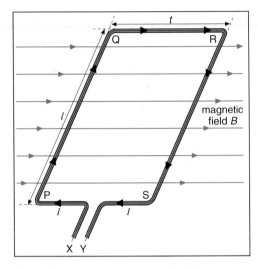

Figure 18.1 Current enters the coil at X and leaves at Y

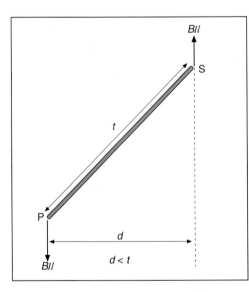

Figure 18.2 Perpendicular separation of forces decreases as the coil turns

Figure 18.3 The brushes and commutator reverse the current through the coil every half turn

Forces on a coil of wire in a magnetic field

Figure 18.1 shows a rectangular loop of wire. The current flows in four different directions through the uniform magnetic field. There is no force exerted on the sides QR and SP, as these are parallel to the magnetic field. Using Fleming's left-hand rule you can see that side PQ experiences a downward force and side RS an upward force.

With the loop pivoted about its centre, these two equal, opposite and parallel forces produce a couple that turns the loop anticlockwise.

As the loop turns, the magnitude and direction of the forces acting on PQ and RS remain constant, while their perpendicular separation decreases (Figure 18.2). The moment acting on the loop decreases as the loop turns.

In an electric **motor**, the coil has to rotate continuously. This poses a major design problem. It has to be arranged for the forces acting on the two sides to change direction each time the coil passes through its vertical position, i.e. every half turn. This is achieved by reversing the current through the coil using a rotating switch, involving a split-ring commutator rotating inside stationary brushes, as shown in Figure 18.3.

Coils rotating in magnetic fields
- Connect an a.c. generator directly to a microvoltmeter. Observe the reading as you slowly turn the generator.
- Connect the generator to an oscilloscope with a slow timebase. Sketch the trace obtained.
- Observe the effect of turning the generator faster and faster. (Try using a hand drill on its axle.)

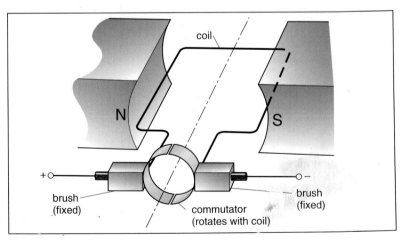

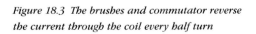

Generators

If you rotate a coil continuously in a magnetic field, you continually change the flux linking the coil. The flux first increases through the coil one way, and then increases through the coil the other way. This induces an alternating voltage, which continually changes direction.

If your connections to a rotating coil were by fixed wires, they would soon be twisted up. But Figure 18.4 shows a **generator**, which has slip rings that connect to the coil to allow it to rotate continuously inside stationary brushes.

Generators in power stations provide our electric mains supply. They produce alternating voltages and currents – voltages and currents that continually change direction.

If you connect an oscilloscope to an a.c. generator, it displays an alternating, sinusoidal trace whose amplitude and frequency increase with the rate of rotation (Figure 18.5).

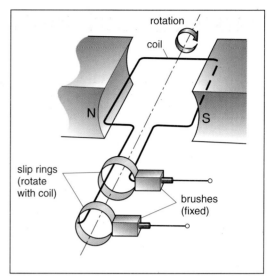

Figure 18.4 Slip ring generator

Making a motor do work

- Connect an ammeter in series with a 12 V motor and its supply. Record the current flowing as the motor spins freely.
- Use a piece of wood rubbing on the motor's axle to slow it down. What happens to the current?

E.m.f. induced across a motor armature

The rotating coil in a motor is called an armature. An armature has a very low resistance. However, only a small current flows through it when it is connected to its power supply and spinning freely. As it spins, its own coil rotates in the magnetic field of the motor. This induces an e.m.f. in the coil of the motor. As you would expect from Lenz's law, the e.m.f. induced across the spinning coil opposes the flow of current through the motor.

If you slow the motor down, you reduce the rate of change of flux through the rotating coil. This reduces the e.m.f. induced in the coil. Slowing the rate of rotation results in a smaller induced e.m.f. and an increased current in the motor.

If you stop a motor completely, there is no induced e.m.f. in the coil. The current is limited by the resistance of the coil only, and can be large enough to burn out the motor.

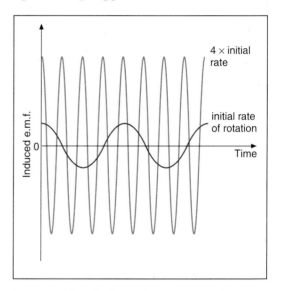

Figure 18.5 Amplitude and frequency depend on rate of rotation

19 Sinusoidal variations

Simple harmonic motion

You learnt much about **s.h.m.** in Chapters 12, 13 and 14 of *Matter and Waves*. All that work is relevant here, so you should re-read those chapters now. Table 19.1 lists important equations from this earlier work on s.h.m.

You know that $T = 1/f$, where f is the frequency. So

$$\omega = 2\pi/T = 2\pi f$$

Table 19.2 lists some of the equations from Table 19.1 expressed in terms of frequency f rather than angular velocity ω.

Table 19.1 *Some s.h.m. equations (all symbols have their usual meanings)*

acceleration	$a = -\omega^2 x$
period	$T = 2\pi/\omega$
displacement	$x = x_0 \cos(\omega t)$
maximum velocity	$v_{max} = \omega x_0$
maximum acceleration	$a_{max} = \omega^2 x_0$
for a mass–spring system	$T = 2\pi\sqrt{(m/k)}$
for a pendulum	$T = 2\pi\sqrt{(l/g)}$

Table 19.2 *Some s.h.m. equations in terms of freqency*

acceleration	$a = -(2\pi f)^2 x$
displacement	$x = x_0 \cos(2\pi f t)$
maximum velocity	$v_{max} = 2\pi f x_0$
maximum acceleration	$a_{max} = (2\pi f)^2 x_0$

A.c. supplies

As you saw in the last chapter, many alternating voltages vary **sinusoidally** with time, in an identical way to the displacement of a harmonic oscillator. You can use an s.h.m. equation to describe how such a voltage V varies with time:

$$V = V_0 \cos(2\pi f t)$$

where V_0 is the maximum value of the voltage. When this voltage V is placed across a resistance R, an alternating current I flows:

$$I = V/R = [V_0 \cos(2\pi f t)]/R = (V_0/R) \cos(2\pi f t)$$

V_0/R is the maximum voltage divided by the resistance. It is the maximum current I_0:

$$I = I_0 \cos(2\pi f t) \qquad \text{where} \qquad V_0/I_0 = R$$

Alternating signals

- Connect the sinusoidal output of a signal generator to an oscilloscope (Figure 19.1). Measure the signal's peak voltage V_0. Use the timebase to calculate its frequency, f.
- Repeat for a signal having a different voltage and frequency.

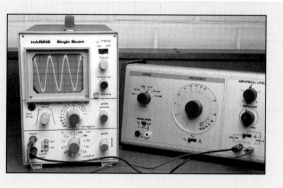

Figure 19.1 *The oscilloscope displays the sinusoidal nature of the alternating supply*

Average values

A sinusoidal trace is symmetrical about the time axis. Its average value is zero. But if an alternating voltage lights a lamp, it would be meaningless to say that the lamp was being lit by an average voltage of 0 V. Similarly, there is no point in stating that the average current through it is 0 A. Nor does it help to refer to the maximum values, V_0 and I_0, since these only occur twice, very briefly, during each cycle.

Comparing a.c. and d.c. supplies

- Set up the circuit shown in Figure 19.2. Turn the switch so that the d.c. supply lights the lamp. Adjust the supply until the voltmeter reads 2 V. Note the brightness of the lamp.
- Switch to the a.c. supply and adjust its output until the lamp lights to approximately the same brightness as before. Flick the switch quickly between its two positions. Finely adjust the output of the a.c. supply until there is no noticeable change in the lamp's brightness between the two switch positions.

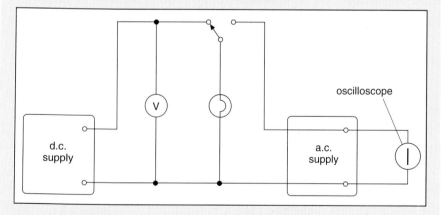

Figure 19.2 *The switch determines which supply lights the lamp*

- Use the oscilloscope to measure V_0, the maximum value of the alternating voltage.
- Repeat for a range of d.c. voltages up to the working voltage of the lamp.
- Plot a graph of peak a.c. voltage against its equivalent d.c. voltage. Calculate the gradient of your graph.

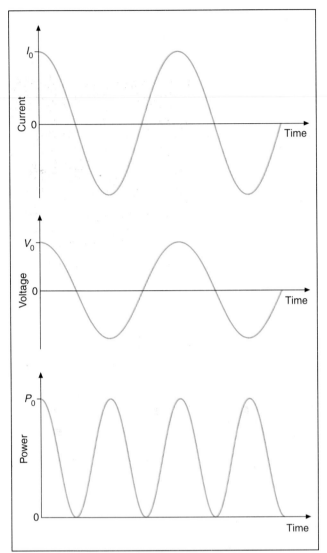

Figure 19.3 At any instant, current and voltage have the same sign; their product is always positive

R.m.s. values

An alternating voltage of peak value V_0 is equivalent to a direct voltage $V_0/\sqrt{2}$:

peak a.c. voltage = $\sqrt{2}$ × equivalent d.c. voltage

To light a 12 V car headlamp fully, a peak a.c. voltage of 17 V ($\sqrt{2}$ × 12 V) is required. We say that such an a.c. supply has an equivalent d.c., or root mean square (r.m.s.), voltage of 12 V:

peak a.c. voltage = $\sqrt{2}$ × r.m.s. voltage
or $V_0 = \sqrt{2} \times V_{rms}$

so $V_{rms} = V_0/\sqrt{2}$

A.c. power supplies and components are labelled with r.m.s. values. The frequency of the mains is 50 Hz. Its r.m.s. voltage is 230 V, so that its peak voltage is 325 V ($\sqrt{2}$ × 230 V):

$$V_{mains} = V_0 \cos (2\pi ft) = 325 \cos(100\pi t)$$

A.c. power

If a 60 W lamp is connected to the 230 V r.m.s. mains supply, the r.m.s. current is I = power/V = 60/230 = 0.26 A. The peak current is

$$I_0 = 0.26 \times \sqrt{2} = 0.37 \text{ A}$$

So the current through the lamp can be described by the equation:

$$I = I_0 \cos(2\pi ft) = 0.37 \cos(100\pi t)$$

Figure 19.3 shows how the current, voltage and power for this lamp vary with time:

power = current × voltage

The maximum power delivered to the lamp by the alternating supply is equal to maximum voltage × maximum current. So

maximum power = $V_0 I_0$ = 325 V × 0.37 A = 120 W

The power varies from zero to a maximum. The average power is 60 W:

average power = $\frac{1}{2}$ × maximum power = $\frac{1}{2}V_0 I_0$

Solid Materials Topic

Metals and magnetism

You know from *Matter and Waves* that materials deform when you apply stresses to them. If the stresses are low, stress is proportional to strain. For small stresses, a material will deform elastically and return to its original length if the stress is removed. For large stresses, materials often deform plastically. They have a permanent deformation, which remains if the stress is removed. You might like to revise the rest of Chapter 5 of *Matter and Waves* before starting this topic.

Figure M1 Crystals of platinum

The structure of metals

In Chapter 3 of *Matter and Waves* you learnt about the structure of solid materials. *Crystalline* materials consist of identical atoms arranged in a regular structure. Crystals have *long-range order*; the arrangement of the atoms is regular over many layers of atoms. If you allow metals to solidify slowly, they form large crystals (Figure M1).

Stretching atomic bonds

The atoms in a metal crystal are linked together by non-directional bonds. When you stretch or compress a metal, you stretch or compress the bonds between the atoms in that metal. The top graph in Figure M2 shows how the force between two atoms varies with the separation r between them. The atoms are in equilibrium when their separation is r_0, where the resultant force between the atoms is zero: there is a balance between attraction and repulsion. The graph shows repulsive forces as positive, since these cause an *increase* in separation, and attractive forces as negative since these cause a *decrease* in separation.

As the separation of the atoms gets less than r_0, the repulsive force between them increases, which pushes them apart. When the atoms are further apart than r_0, there is then an attractive force between the atoms, which pulls them back together. Up to a point, the attractive force increases in magnitude as the separation gets larger. But if the separation gets too large, the attractive force starts to decrease. It gets rapidly weaker. When the atoms are a long way apart, the bond between them is broken and there are no forces between the atoms.

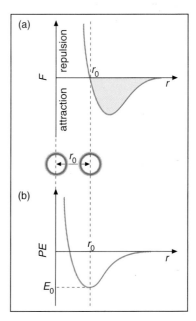

Figure M2 At the equilibrium separation, the resultant force between the atoms is zero and potential energy is minimum

Hooke's law

Figure M3 magnifies the part of the force–separation graph around the equilibrium separation r_0. Around the place where the line crosses the axis, it is approximately a straight line. For small increases or decreases in separation, the force is proportional to the displacement:

$$F \propto x$$

This behaviour is Hooke's law, which you studied in Chapter 4 of *Matter and Waves*.

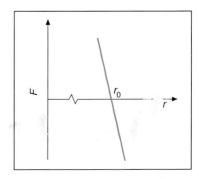

Figure M3 Around the equilibrium separation, force is proportional to displacement

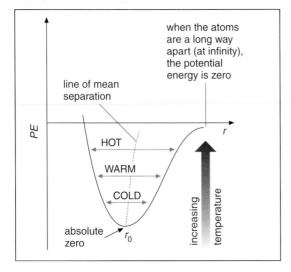

Figure M4 *Above absolute zero, the atoms oscillate about their equilibrium separation*

Energy–separation graphs

Underneath the force–separation graph in Figure M2 is an energy–separation graph. This shows how the potential energy stored in the bond between the two atoms varies with separation between the atoms. Just like the graphs of electrical potential (Chapter 8), this graph shows that the atoms have zero potential energy when the atoms are a long way apart from each other.

When the separation is greater than r_0, atoms attract each other. As they get closer, their potential energy decreases. It is a minimum when the atoms are at their equilibrium separation. As the separation decreases below the equilibrium separation, the potential energy increases once more as the atoms repel.

Thermal expansion

Figure M4 magnifies part of the energy–separation graph around the equilibrium separation. If the atoms connected by this bond are at a temperature of absolute zero, the atoms are at rest at their equilibrium separation.

If the atoms are above absolute zero, they have more energy and they can oscillate. The curve at the bottom of this graph is not symmetrical. As the blue lines show, the atoms oscillate outwards by a larger distance than they oscillate inwards. So their new mean position is greater than the equilibrium separation r_0. At higher temperatures, their mean separation increases even further. This behaviour is *thermal expansion*.

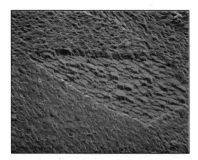

Figure M5 *Etching on the surface of a polycrystalline substance. You can see the boundaries between the crystals*

Polycrystalline and amorphous

Most metals are *polycrystalline*. They are made of many crystals aligned randomly (Figure M5). The size of the crystals in metals depends on the rate at which metals are cooled. Slow cooling produces large crystals. Fast cooling produces small crystals. The surfaces where the crystal grains join are called *grain boundaries*.

Figure M6 shows a liquid metal sprayed onto a cold spinning cylinder to produce a thin ribbon. Under these circumstances, the cooling rate can exceed 1 MK s^{-1}. If the liquid cools so rapidly that, when it hits the cold surface, the molecules have no time to move into a crystalline structure, the resulting metal is *amorphous*; there is no regular arrangement of the molecules. Ultra-fast cooling can produce amorphous metals.

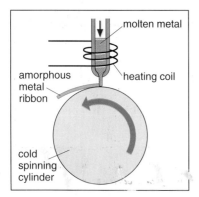

Figure M6 *The jet of molten metal solidifies quickly on the cold spinning cylinder*

Imperfections in metal crystals

If you get an absolutely perfect crystal, the uniformity would lead you to expect tremendous strength. However, getting crystals of metals perfect enough to demonstrate this theoretical strength is very difficult. Most crystals contain irregularities that reduce their strength considerably.

The easiest type of imperfection to understand is called an *edge dislocation*. In a perfect crystal, many identical layers of atoms are stacked on top of each other. Figure M7 shows a crystal containing an edge dislocation. There is an additional half layer of atoms between two complete layers of atoms. If you apply forces as shown, the dislocation moves through the crystal, until it eventually stops at a grain boundary.

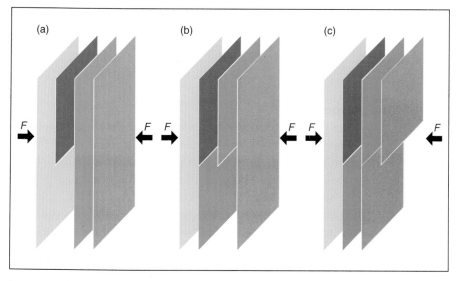

Figure M7 The edge dislocation moves when forces are applied

Slip planes

In the simple crystal structure shown in Figure M8, the dislocations prefer to move along certain planes of atoms, called *slip planes*. Repeated dislocation movement results in certain layers of the crystal sliding over each other, without the crystal breaking apart.

Dislocations get in the way of each other

As you work a material and it deforms plastically, the deformation produces more dislocations. As further plastic deformation takes place, the increasing numbers of dislocations moving along intersecting slip planes start to get in the way of each other. So instead of more dislocations leading to the possibility of more plastic deformation, their tangle makes it *harder* for plastic deformation to take place. The material has become *work-hardened*.

Imperfections stop dislocation movement

The presence of atoms of a different size disrupts the crystal structure and makes it harder for dislocations to move. Carbon in steel makes it harder for the dislocations to move and hence makes the steel less able to deform plastically.

Aluminium alloys used in aircraft rely on the presence of copper and other atoms of different sizes to make the mixture of metals stronger than pure aluminium.

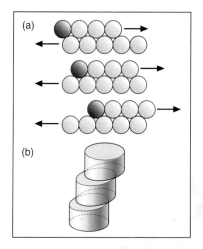

Figure M8 Certain planes of atoms can slip over each other

Grain boundaries stop dislocation movement

In a single metal crystal there are no grain boundaries. If there are dislocations present, these can move a long way through the crystal. They allow the material to deform plastically without breaking, since only one bond is being moved at a time.

In a polycrystalline material with plenty of grain boundaries, the dislocations cannot move very far. So metals with small crystals, and therefore more grain boundaries, are stronger than metals with larger crystals and fewer grain boundaries.

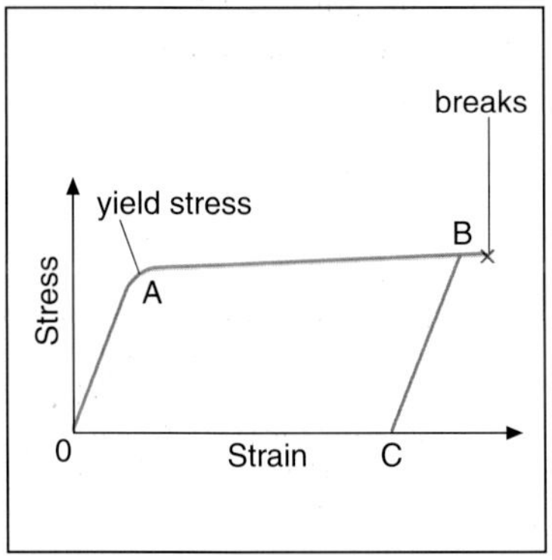

Stretching copper

You learnt in Chapter 6 of *Matter and Waves* how to produce a stress–strain graph for a wire. Figure M9 shows a stress–strain graph for soft copper. The first part of the graph is a straight line. Stress is proportional to strain, and Hooke's law describes this region. The slope of the graph is the Young modulus. For these stresses and strains, no permanent change in the structure of the copper wire occurs. As the wire is stretched, the separations of the atoms increase but the atoms do not change position. When the stress is removed, the wire returns to its original length.

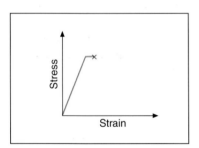

Figure M9 Stress–strain graph for soft copper

Yielding

At point A, the copper starts to deform permanently. Above this stress the dislocations move so that, when the stress is removed, the wire cannot return to its original shape. The stress at which permanent deformation occurs is called the *yield stress*. This is the stress at which dislocations begin to move.

Work-hardening and annealing

At point B, the wire has been stretched nearly to breaking. If the stress is then removed, the wire contracts a little, following the line BC parallel to the first part of the graph. However, the dislocations in the wire have become entangled and only the elastic strain is recovered. The wire is *work-hardened*. If you test a piece of work-hardened copper, you will get a graph like that in Figure M10, which is exactly like the last part of Figure M9. The value of the Young modulus remains the same.

Figure M10 For work-hardened copper, the stress–strain graph is the same as the last part of the graph for soft copper

Pulling a large-diameter copper rod through progressively smaller holes, called dies, produces copper wire. During this process, it becomes work-hardened. If it becomes too hard, it must be softened before it can be drawn into progressively thinner wire. It is heated and allowed to cool in a process called *annealing*. This gives the copper atoms sufficient energy to rearrange themselves and disentangle the dislocations. Annealing returns work-hardened copper to a soft state.

Elastic and plastic deformations

Stress is force/area, and strain is extension/(original length). So

$$\text{stress} \times \text{strain} = (\text{force/area}) \times (\text{extension/original length})$$

$$= (\text{force} \times \text{extension})/(\text{area} \times \text{original length})$$

$$= \text{work done/volume}$$

The area under a stress–strain graph is the work done per unit volume of the wire. This is called the *energy density*.

If, when you stretch and release a wire, it follows the same line on the graph when loading and unloading (Figure M11), the energy density for stretching is the same as for unstretching. So all the energy put in to stretching the wire is returned when the wire is released. The atoms go back to their original positions. An *elastic deformation* is one in which no energy is absorbed during a complete stretching/unstretching cycle. When elastically deformed,

$$\text{energy density} = \tfrac{1}{2} \times \text{stress} \times \text{strain}$$

If the unloading graph is not the same as the loading graph (Figure M12), less energy is released when the wire is unloaded than was needed to load the wire. Some energy is absorbed and permanent deformation is produced. Dislocations have moved the atoms to different positions. This is called *plastic deformation*.

This plastic behaviour shows that copper's dislocations can move easily. Copper is *ductile*: it can be pulled out into wires. It is also *malleable*: it can be beaten into the required shape.

Tough or brittle

Metals are chosen for a combination of their elastic and plastic qualities. For instance, we do not want a car to distort so much when it is full of passengers that its doors will not shut! Using a stiff material, such as steel, when constructing a car's body controls the amount of elastic deformation. But cars are also designed to absorb large amounts of energy by plastic deformation during a car crash by allowing certain regions to crumple.

Soft copper (Figure M9) is *tough*: the area under the graph before it breaks is large. It absorbs large amounts of energy per unit volume before it breaks. Work-hardened copper (Figure M10) is *brittle*. The area under the stress–strain graph is small. It absorbs little energy by plastic deformation before breaking. This is because the dislocations have become entangled and cannot cause further plastic deformation.

The behaviour of steels

Steels are usually produced by mixing iron with varying proportions of carbon. Steels are widely used as engineering materials. They are stiff and relatively cheap. By changing the amount of carbon and the heat treatment they receive, they can be given a wide range of properties.

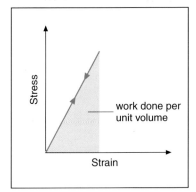

Figure M11 For an elastic deformation, the energy supplied when loading is released when unloading

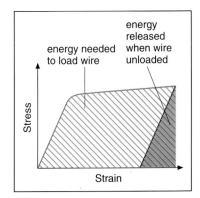

Figure M12 The energy per unit volume absorbed by the wire is the difference between the area cross-hatched in blue and the red area

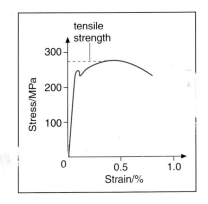

Figure M13 Stress–strain graph for mild steel

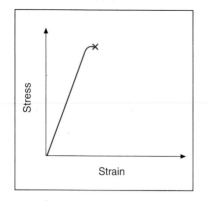

Figure M14 Stress–strain for quench-hardened steel

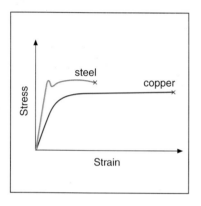

Figure M15 Stress–strain graphs for soft copper and mild steel

Mild steel contains less than 0.25% carbon. The steel used for car bodies contains 0.04 to 0.08% carbon. Its behaviour depends little on its heat treatment. Figure M13 shows a stress–strain graph for mild steel. As with the behaviour of copper, the graph shows elastic behaviour for low stresses, followed by plastic behaviour for larger stresses.

The behaviour of high-carbon steel depends on heat treatment. If it is heated and cooled rapidly by quenching it in cold water (*quench-hardened*), it changes its crystal structure to one in which dislocations cannot move very far, and the steel is hard but brittle. It is used for cutting tools like chisels. Figure M14 shows a graph for quench-hardened high-carbon steel.

If the quench-hardened steel is afterwards reheated slightly and then allowed to cool, the crystal structure begins to change and the steel becomes less hard. It can then be used for hammers and screwdrivers. This softening process is called *tempering*.

Comparing copper and steel

Figure M15 compares the stress–strain graphs for soft copper and mild steel. The *strength* of a material is the stress required to break a material. Steel is stronger than copper.

As you learnt in Chapter 6 of *Matter and Waves*, a *stiff* or *rigid* material has a high Young modulus: it takes a high stress to produce a given strain. A *flexible* material has a low Young modulus: it needs a low stress for a given strain. Figure M15 shows that steel is stiffer than copper: the slope of the stress–strain graph is greater. The Young modulus is a function of atomic bonding: strong bonds produce stiff materials.

Creep and fatigue

Materials can fail due to plastic deformation occurring below the yield stress.

Creep occurs if the strain of a material increases over time even though the stress remains constant. A loaded material creeps if it is above about 0.3 of its absolute melting temperature. For instance, lead sheeting (melting point ≈ 600 K) on sloping roofs creeps; it gradually stretches over time.

If you continually load and unload a material, it can fail, even if the stresses are less than the yield stress. The loading and unloading can produce cracks that gradually get bigger with time. The material eventually breaks. This is called *fatigue*. Fatigue is a big problem with all aluminium alloys used for aircraft bodies. After a time, microscopic cracks build up and, though it may look safe, the airframe can no longer cope with the stresses for which it was designed.

Usually material engineers are able to predict this behaviour, and components are changed before failure occurs.

Both creep and fatigue occur because dislocation movement is a statistical process. At low temperatures and stresses, dislocation movement is less likely but it may still slowly occur.

Paramagnetism and diamagnetism

Materials have magnetic effects, caused mainly by the spinning orbital electrons. Magnetism is induced inside materials when they are put into a magnetic field. They behave as though they have little magnets inside. For most materials, this magnetic effect is small, often hardly noticeable. These are paramagnetic and diamagnetic materials. Paramagnetism and diamagnetism cannot be described in terms of classical physics, which would predict no magnetic effect. They are only described by quantum physics.

When materials are put in a magnetic field, their magnetic spins align according to the field direction. For *paramagnetic* materials, the internal magnetism lines up in the same direction as the external magnetic field. For a *diamagnetic* material, the internal magnetism lines up opposing the external magnetic field. Magnets therefore attract paramagnetic materials, and repel diamagnetic materials.

If you pour liquid oxygen between the poles of a strong magnet, it will stick between the poles, showing its paramagnetism. Aluminium and many other metals are paramagnetic.

Water and most organic compounds are diamagnetic, as are many non-metals. Some metals are diamagnetic, such as bismuth, copper, gold, silver and lead, with bismuth being the strongest.

Paramagnetic and diamagnetic effects are small. But if you balance a glass rod on a watch glass, you can demonstrate that it is diamagnetic – a strong magnet will repel the glass (Figure M16).

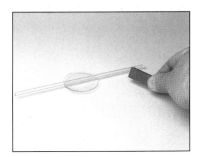

Figure M16 The magnet repels the glass rod

Ferromagnetism

Strong magnetism is produced by *ferromagnetic* materials. These are permanently magnetic; their magnetism is not induced by the external magnetic field. Iron, of course, is ferromagnetic. So are cobalt, nickel and many alloys. You can read about the magnetic domains associated with ferromagnetism in Chapter 10.

In hard magnetic materials, it is difficult to rotate the domains. So it is difficult to magnetise the materials, and difficult to demagnetise them. Such materials make good permanent magnets.

In soft magnetic materials, it is easy to rotate the domains. So it is easy to magnetise them and easy to demagnetise them. Such materials make good electromagnets and transformer cores. Certain amorphous metals are extremely good soft magnetic materials.

The Curie temperature

If you raise the temperature sufficiently, a ferromagnetic material will lose its ferromagnetism. It then becomes paramagnetic – much less magnetic. The temperature at which this happens is called the *Curie temperature*. If the temperature drops below the Curie temperature, the ferromagnetism returns.

SOLID MATERIALS TOPIC

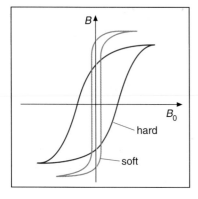

Figure M17 Magnetic hysteresis loops for hard and soft magnetic materials

Investigating magnetic materials

You can use a solenoid to investigate the magnetic properties of a material. Compare the magnetic field produced with the ferromagnetic sample inside the solenoid (B) with that produced without the sample (B_0). The relative permeability of the sample is the ratio B to B_0.

Figure M17 illustrates repeated magnetising and demagnetising of two different magnetic materials. The area enclosed by the curves is proportional to the energy needed to magnetise and demagnetise them per cycle. The blue loop is for a soft magnetic material. The area enclosed by that loop is relatively small, because it needs little energy – it is easy – to magnetise and demagnetise. When magnetised, it makes the stronger magnet: you can see its value of B is larger. The red loop is the hard magnetic material. The area enclosed by the loop is relatively large: it needs more energy – it is harder – to magnetise and demagnetise it. Its magnetism is more permanent, but not as strong.

Polymers and dielectrics

The structures of polymers

As you learnt in Chapter 6 of *Matter and Waves*, polymers consist of long chain molecules. If the molecules are randomly arranged, the polymer is *amorphous*. The other type of polymer is *semicrystalline*: the arrangement is partly random and partly ordered. It is not possible to make perfectly crystalline polymers.

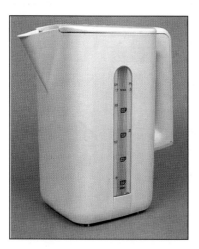

Figure M18 This electric kettle is made from extruded thermoplastic

Thermoplastics

The molecules in a polymer are strong. The bonds *along* the chains are hard to break. But these bonds are not the only bonds within polymers. There are forces *between* the chains in a polymer.

In some polymers, the only bonds between the chains are weak forces called *van der Waals forces*. At low temperatures, the van der Waals forces restrict movement of the chains. But at higher temperatures, the molecules have sufficient energy to rotate or move past each other. This allows the chains to rearrange.

These polymers are called *thermoplastics*. They are elastic at low temperatures, but they become plastic at higher temperatures, when the van der Waals bonds melt. Thermoplastics are widely used for moulding consumer items (Figure M18). They are usually delivered to a manufacturer as sacks of granules, which can be heated to melt them before they are injected into a mould, or extruded (squeezed through a nozzle) to produce a finished item.

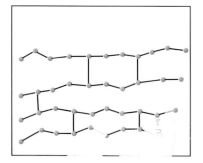

Figure M19 .... polymer

Thermosets

In some plastics there are strong, permanent links between the chains called *crosslinks* (Figure M19). Such links fix the arrangement of the polymer chains at all temperatures. These plastics are called *thermosets*. Thermosets are rigid, whatever the temperature. In the first thermosets, the crosslinks were formed by a chemical reaction that was triggered by temperature, hence the name thermosets. But now there are many thermosets whose crosslinks are formed at low temperature.

Amorphous thermoplastics

Perspex is a typical amorphous thermoplastic. Its chains have no order in their arrangement. Figure M20 shows a transparent telephone made of Perspex. It is rigid at room temperature because the chains are not free to move.

The red graph in Figure M21 shows a stress–strain graph for Perspex at room temperature. Perspex obeys Hooke's law, and is elastic. If you remove the stress, the Perspex will return to its original shape. If Perspex at room temperature is stretched beyond its elastic limit, it will break. At room temperature, Perspex is brittle; its behaviour is like glass.

If you raise the temperature of Perspex, you weaken the van der Waals bonding. Eventually you reach the *glass transition temperature*. Below this temperature, Perspex behaves like glass. It will bounce like a glass marble, but shatter if hit too hard.

Around the glass transition temperature, you can distort Perspex, but then it gradually returns to its original shape. The movement of the chains is very viscous and they absorb energy when they move. A Perspex ball at the glass transition temperature has a very poor bounce.

Above the glass transition temperature, Perspex is rubbery. It will bounce like a rubber ball. If you increase the temperature further, Perspex gets softer and eventually it loses its shape and can be moulded.

Figure M20 The components of this telephone can be seen through its Perspex case

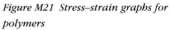

Figure M21 Stress–strain graphs for polymers

Semicrystalline thermoplastics

Polyethene (polythene or polyethylene) is a typical semicrystalline thermoplastic, as is nylon. In both, there is some regular arrangement of the chain molecules. The arrangement of the chains depends on the way that the polymer is made and shaped.

The green graph on Figure M21 shows a stress–strain graph for polyethene. During the first part of the graph, polyethene is elastic, and obeys Hooke's law. As the stress increases, polyethene distorts plastically. In the tangled, amorphous regions, the chains stretch out along the direction of the tension (Figure M22). As the stretching proceeds, the chains become more aligned. At this stage it is harder to stretch polyethene, and the graph becomes steeper.

In the stress is removed after stretching, the polyethene does not return to its original length, but remains with the chains still partly uncoiled.

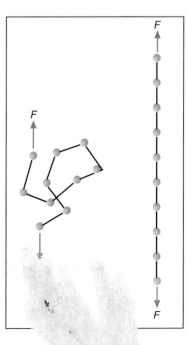

Figure M22 It is easier to stretch a coiled m... than a straight one

Cold-drawn polyethene tape is used for strapping boxes. It consists of polyethene in which all the chains lie along the length of the tape. It is very hard to stretch cold-drawn polyethene tape because the molecules are strong. But it is easy to pull it apart sideways, because the bonds between the chains are very weak.

Rigid thermosets

Epoxy resin and Melamine are two typical thermosetting plastics. Epoxy resin is commonly used as an adhesive. It is made from a viscous liquid of chain molecules, which forms strong and permanent crosslinks when a chemical hardener is added. The resulting plastic is very strong and rigid. Melamine is another thermoset sometimes used to make the durable surface of kitchen worktops.

Thermosetting plastics cannot be distorted at higher temperatures. Their strong permanent crosslinks are much stronger than the weak van der Waals bonds in thermoplastics. Once they have been formed, their shape is fixed and cannot be changed without destroying the structure, e.g. by machining. Thermosets are amorphous. They cannot undergo plastic deformation, so they are brittle. They have graphs similar to the red line in Figure M21.

Elastomers

An *elastomer* is a material that returns to its original shape when a distorting force is removed. Rubber is an elastomer. It is an amorphous polymer with some crosslinks. In unstretched rubber, the long chains are coiled and tangled up. As you stretch the rubber, the chains straighten out. The stress–strain graph for stretching rubber is the blue graph in Figure M21. This is shown enlarged with an unloading graph in Figure M23. The loading graph gets steeper as the stress increases: it gets harder to stretch the rubber as the chains straighten out. But when the rubber is unloaded, the chain molecules coil up again, and the rubber returns to its original length. The stress–strain graph for unloading is below the graph for loading.

The area under the stress–strain graph is the work done per unit volume, the energy density. The work done on the rubber when it is stretched (the blue hatched area) is greater than the work done by the rubber when it returns to its original length (the red area). The area between the two graphs is the energy absorbed per unit volume during the stretching and releasing process. This behaviour is called *hysteresis*. Each time the rubber is stretched and released, energy is absorbed by the rubber. It makes the rubber hot, which then heats the surroundings. Hysteresis losses in rubber tyres account for a proportion of the energy needed to power a car.

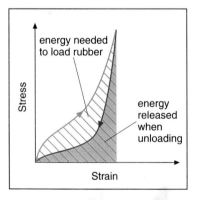

Figure M23 Stress–strain graph for rubber

Insulators and dielectrics

Most polymers are insulators. Electric currents do not flow through them. But all insulators, apart from a vacuum, contain charged particles and the charged particles have electrical effects. The electrical effects are noticeable when you use insulators between the plates of a capacitor.

Dipoles

The charged particles in many insulators are not evenly distributed. In some parts of the material there is a surplus of electrons, and that part of the insulator is negative. In other parts of the insulator, there is a shortage of electrons, and that part of the insulator is positive. On balance, unless the insulator is charged, the positive and negative parts have equal charge, and the net charge of the insulator is zero.

Pure water is an insulator and the water molecules that it contains have positive and negative regions (Figure M24). The two parts, the positive and the negative *poles*, mean that the molecule is a *dipole* (from the Greek for 'two poles'). Water molecules are always dipoles; they are *permanent dipoles*. Water molecules attract each other.

The electron clouds in single atoms are arranged symmetrically about the nucleus. So isolated atoms have no poles – they are not polar. But if the atom is in an electric field, this slightly displaces the electron cloud relative to the nucleus and again produces positive and negative poles (Figure M25). Dipoles produced like this are called *induced dipoles*.

Relative permittivity

The insulating material between the plates of a capacitor is called a *dielectric*. If the dielectric is an insulator other than a vacuum, the permanent or induced dipoles between the plates align themselves with any field produced by the plates. This repels more electrons from the positive plate and attracts more electrons on to the negative plate than would be the case if there were a vacuum between the plates. So, for the same voltage across the plates, more charge is stored by the capacitor (i.e. more charge is moved from one plate to the other) than if there were a vacuum between the plates. Therefore, the capacitance is greater. The ratio between the capacitance with an insulator to the capacitance with a vacuum is called the *relative permittivity* ε_r of the dielectric.

Water is highly polar; it has a relative permittivity of about 80. But some ceramic materials are much more polar and have relative permittivities of thousands.

Dielectric losses

Energy is needed to rotate the dipoles of an insulator when an electric field is applied. Not all of this energy is returned to the power supply when the field is removed, and some of it is spread randomly in the dielectric, raising its internal energy. If the electric field alternates, a significant increase in the temperature of a dielectric may be observable. Losses like this from the electric circuit to the dielectric are called *dielectric losses*. For many ceramic and other materials used in capacitors, dielectric losses are low. But the dielectric losses do depend on frequency, in general increasing with increasing frequency. It is hard to find dielectric materials that are not lossy at very high frequencies. Capacitors for use at high frequencies often use air between their plates for this reason.

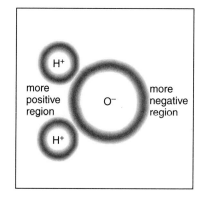

Figure M24 A water dipole

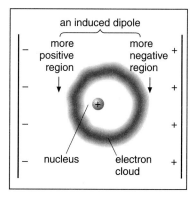

Figure M25 In an electric field, the electron cloud shifts relative to the nucleus, producing an induced dipole

For many plastics, dielectric losses are significant at least at some frequencies. These losses may be used deliberately to produce *dielectric heating*, for instance for industrial processes like welding plastics.

Dielectric losses are significant in water at any frequency, but when water is in electric fields oscillating at frequencies of about 2500 MHz, large-amplitude vibrations occur due to resonance of bonds within the water molecule. This process is very lossy – it takes large amounts of energy from the field and raises the temperature of the water. This is the principle used in the microwave oven, and explains why they only cook properly foods containing water.

Materials technology

Combining materials

Many pure materials are strong, but their individual properties are not fitted for every task. Materials technologists combine different materials to make the best use of their different properties.

Stopping cracks

You know that cracks reduce the strength of many objects. A crack in a glass window can spread right across it. Ships have sunk as a result of cracks spreading right across them.

Photoelastic stress analysis is a technique for examining the stress in, for example, a Perspex model. It uses light and polarising filters. You know from Chapter 17 of *Matter and Waves* that two polarising filters at right angles will not let light through. But if you place a piece of Perspex between the two filters, as shown in Figure M26, the Perspex will rotate the plane of polarisation of light by an amount that depends on the stress in the Perspex. So you can see a pattern in the Perspex that corresponds to the stress.

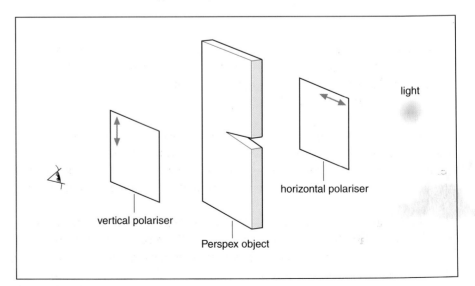

Figure M26 The Perspex rotates the plane of polarisation of the light

Perspex is a material used widely in schools to demonstrate stress analysis. Figure M27 shows a much more sophisticated stress analysis experiment involving polycarbonate plastic and circular polarizers positioned either side of the sample. At the tip of the crack, there is a maximum stress when the material is stretched. The material fails at this *stress concentration* and the crack gets bigger. The tip of the crack moves through the material and the crack gets larger.

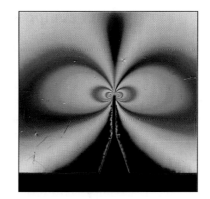

Figure M27 The photoelastic stress analysis shows the stress concentration at the tip of the crack

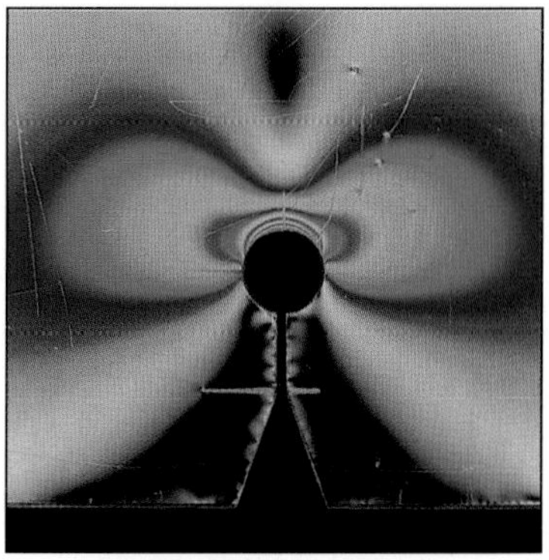

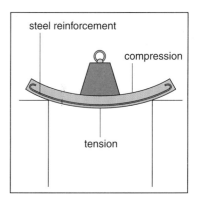

Figure M28 Drilling a hole at the end of the crack reduces the stress concentration

You can reduce the danger of cracks by using a material that can undergo plastic deformation and survive the cracks. Tough materials in which dislocations are free to move, like copper and mild steel, are less troubled by cracks than brittle materials like glass or cast iron. Thermoplastics are less likely to crack above their glass transition temperature, where they are tougher.

If you do have a crack in a material, you can reduce the stress concentration at the tip of a crack by drilling a hole there. Figure M28 shows a photoelastic stress pattern for a polycarbonate sample with a hole drilled at the end of the crack.

Reinforced concrete

Concrete is cheap and moderately strong in compression. Steel is quite cheap and strong in tension and compression. If you put steel rods in concrete, then the steel can take the tension and the concrete the compression. Reinforced concrete beams are used to span gaps in walls. When a load is placed on the beam, it bends as shown in Figure M29. The bottom of the beam is under tension and the top is under compression. Reinforced beams in this situation have the steel at the bottom to take the tension, and the concrete at the top takes the compression.

Prestressed reinforced concrete is an improvement on normal reinforced concrete. With normal reinforced concrete, the reinforcing rods hold the structure together when tension is applied to that part, but, as the steel stretches, the concrete around it cracks.

With prestressed concrete, the steel reinforcements are first stretched, as shown in Figure M30. Concrete is then cast around the stretched reinforcements. When the concrete is set, the stretching force is removed from the reinforcements and these contract, putting the concrete into *compression*.

When prestressed beams are used, loads applied cause the reinforcements to be stretched again, but not enough to remove all the compressive stress on the concrete. The result is that the concrete never gets into tension and therefore never cracks.

Figure M29 The beam is in compression at the top and tension at the bottom

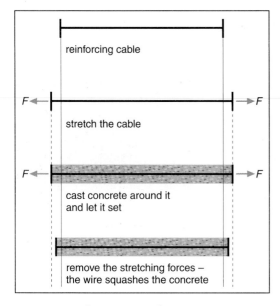

Figure M30 *Making prestressed reinforced concrete*

Other composite materials

Wood is strong in tension along the grain and weak across the grain. It is comparatively weak in compression because the fibres collapse. Plywood is made from alternate layers of wood with the grain going in opposite directions (Figure M31, top). In this way it has good strength in both directions. Chipboard has chips of wood randomly oriented and glued together to give strength in all directions (Figure M31, bottom).

Rigid thermosetting polymers are strong but brittle. They can be reinforced by mixing strong fibres in them before they harden. In glass-reinforced plastic (GRP), glass fibres are mixed into a synthetic resin such as epoxy. This produces a composite material that is strong and tough. Toughness depends on the interface between the fibres and the resin being comparatively weak so that the crack is blunted when it meets the interface. The interfaces act as crack stoppers. Wood is tough across the grain but brittle along it because of the weak interface between the fibres. Carbon-fibre-reinforced composites are even stronger (Figure M32).

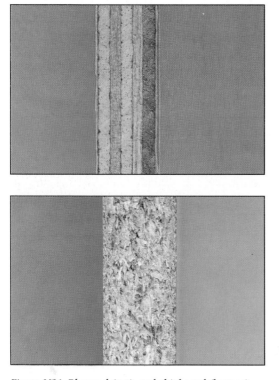

Figure M31 *Plywood (top) and chipboard (bottom)*

Figure M32 *Carbon-fibre squash racquet*

Earth and Atmosphere Topic

The Earth

Determining age

You know how old you are because your date of birth is written on your birth certificate, but how do you set about finding the age of the Earth, whose beginning was not witnessed or recorded? Consider trees. Birch trees live for about 40 years, so someone may well remember when such a tree was planted or first appeared. But oaks can live up to 1500 years, and bristlecone pines (Figure E1) for almost 5000 years. How are these ages known?

Figure E1 The bristlecone pine is the world's longest-living species of tree

A tree's age is found by counting the annual growth rings in its trunk. The width of each ring tells us about that year's climatic conditions. Scientists have assembled a databank of ring information dating back 4000 years. The ring patterns of samples – taken from, say, wooden beams in old houses – are matched to this, allowing an approximate age to be determined.

Geological dating

Dating of older artefacts, e.g. Stone Age tools or dinosaur bones, is obtained by using geological data. During the nineteenth century, geologists constructed a relative timescale based on fossils found in different strata, the lowest strata being the oldest. Such geological time was divided into four broad eras, each subdivided into periods and epochs (Table E1).

Table E1 *Geological time eras and periods*

Era	Period	Dates/Myr ago
Cainozoic	Quaternary	now–2.5
	Tertiary	2.5–65
Mesozoic	Cretaceous	65–136
	Jurassic	136–195
	Triassic	195–225
Palaeozoic	Permian	225–280
	Carboniferous	280–345
	Devonian	345–395
	Silurian	395–430
	Ordovician	430–500
	Cambrian	500–570
Pre-Cambrian		570–4650

Uranium (U) isotope dating

How do we estimate the age of the Earth itself? The discovery of *radioactivity*, and more importantly its *exponential decay law* (1902), provided the means by which a *radioactive timescale* could be added to geological time.

All rocks containing uranium have the *isotopes* ^{235}U and ^{238}U present in the same ratio:

(number of ^{238}U atoms)/(number of ^{235}U atoms) = 138

Present astrophysical theories indicate that, when uranium is formed in stellar explosions, this ratio is only 0.7. Why has it increased with time?

In Chapter 10 of *Matter and Waves*, you learnt that the number of atoms N of a decaying isotope remaining after a time t is given by

EARTH AND ATMOSPHERE TOPIC

Table E2 *Half-lives of two uranium isotopes*

Isotope	Half-life, $t_{1/2}$/years
uranium-235, ^{235}U	0.7×10^9
uranium-238, ^{238}U	4.5×10^9

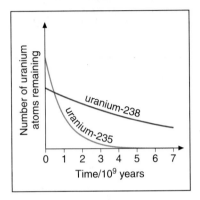

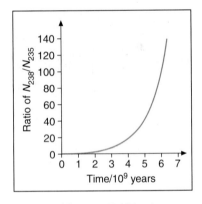

Figure E2 ^{235}U *has a shorter half-life than* ^{238}U

Figure E3 *The ratio* N_{238}/N_{235} *increases with time as* ^{238}U *decays slower*

where N_0 is the initial number of atoms present and λ is the decay constant for the isotope, and also that

$$\lambda = (\ln 2)/t_{1/2} \qquad (\ln 2 = 0.693)$$

where $t_{1/2}$ is the *half-life* of the isotope.

Isotopes of uranium have extremely long half-lives (Table E2). ^{235}U has a greater decay rate than ^{238}U. Figure E2 shows that the number of ^{235}U atoms falls faster than the number of ^{238}U atoms. Hence, the ratio of N_{238}/N_{235} increases with time. We can calculate how long this process takes. Since

$$N_{238} = (N_{238})_0 \, e^{-\lambda_{238} t} \qquad \text{and} \qquad N_{235} = (N_{235})_0 \, e^{-\lambda_{235} t}$$

their ratio is

$$N_{238}/N_{235} = [(N_{238})_0/(N_{235})_0] \, e^{[(\lambda_{235} - \lambda_{238})t]}$$

Figure E3 shows how this ratio varies with time. The graph shows that it takes 6.5×10^9 years for the ratio of ^{238}U to ^{235}U atoms to increase from 0.7 to 138.

If the Earth's uranium atoms were formed in a stellar explosion 6500 million years ago, and the Earth took time to form from the debris of this stellar explosion, the Earth is obviously younger than this!

These figures are estimates. They rely on some data that are not precisely known and assume that the physical processes involved have been uniform since the universe began. But within the expected limits of accuracy, these figures agree with other astronomical estimates of the age of the universe.

Lead (Pb) isotope dating

^{207}Pb is the final decay product of ^{235}U, and ^{206}Pb is the final decay product of ^{238}U. Any uranium-bearing rock will therefore also contain these two isotopes of lead. Unfortunately, not all of this lead will have been produced since the rock was formed. The debris from which the Earth was made already contained an amount of these lead isotopes. Indeed, they are found in uranium-free, lead-bearing rocks, along with another isotope, ^{204}Pb.

Using the constant ratio of these three lead isotopes in uranium-free and uranium-rich rocks, we can find the amounts of ^{206}Pb and ^{207}Pb that have resulted from the decay of uranium within the rock. In turn, this allows the ratio of the uranium isotopes at the time the rock solidified to be calculated.

Care is definitely needed in interpreting such data. It is possible that the lead isotopes were produced by the decay of something else in addition to uranium. It is also possible that they may have been added to ___ arrival of a meteorite. However, adopting this method suggests that the ___ is about 4.5×10^9 years.

The shape and size of the Earth

Pythagoras (500 BC) suggested that the Earth was spherical. Eratosthenes (200 BC) measured its circumference by using the angle cast by a shadow in Alexandria at the exact instant that the Sun was immediately overhead, due south, in Aswan. The distance between these towns was known: it had been measured by Roman legions.

Use the data from Figure E4 to calculate a value for the circumference, and hence the radius R_E, of the Earth. Compare your value for the radius with the currently accepted value ($R_E = 6400$ km).

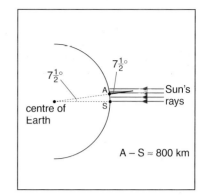

Figure E4 Eratosthenes' data

What is the Earth made of?

The measurement of the universal gravitational constant by Cavendish in 1798 led to a value of 6×10^{24} kg for the Earth's mass (see Chapter 2). Combining the values for mass and radius gives an average density of 5500 kg m^{-3}. The average density of the rocks making up the Earth's *crust* is only 2700 kg m^{-3}. The density of the water covering approximately 70% of the Earth's surface is just over 1000 kg m^{-3}.

What makes the average density so high? What is inside the Earth?

Evidence from earthquakes

Earthquakes result from the stresses set up by the movements of the plates making up the Earth's crust. They occur at boundaries between the plates. Plates moving towards each other set up large compressive stresses. Plates sliding past each other (Figure E5) sometimes interlock. Enormous quantities of energy are stored in compressed rocks. When the plates give way, this energy is suddenly released. Shock waves travel away from the point of origin, the *focus*. They can travel great distances through and around the Earth. The point on the Earth's surface directly above the focus is called the *epicentre*.

Figure E5 The San Andreas Fault (SAF), California – arrows show the direction in which the plates are sliding

Instruments called *seismographs* are used to detect shock waves. Most contain a heavy sprung mass, *M*, which remains stationary during an earthquake while the rest of the instrument, which is rigidly fixed to the Earth, vibrates. They are calibrated using carefully controlled man-made explosions.

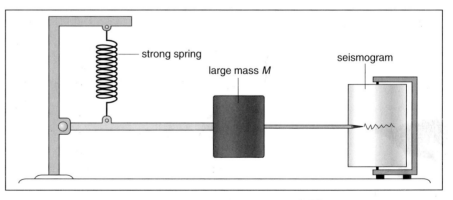

Figure E   is seismograph detects vertical   ns of the Earth

Ea   station has three such instruments set up to record the Earth's vib   n north–south, east–west and vertical directions (Figure E6). Vib   s are recorded onto a *seismogram* (Figure E7). Recordings from at lea   ee well-separated stations are needed to pinpoint the position of an epicentre.

P-waves and S-waves

Figure E7 shows a typical seismogram. It shows a number of different shock waves. The *primary wave* (P-wave) is the first to arrive. It is a longitudinal pressure wave that travels through the Earth. The *secondary wave* (S-wave) is the next to arrive. It is a transverse wave that travels more slowly through the Earth. Surface waves are then detected. These are transverse and called either Rayleigh or Love waves according to their direction of vibration.

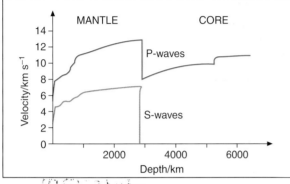

Figure E8 Variation of wave speed with depth

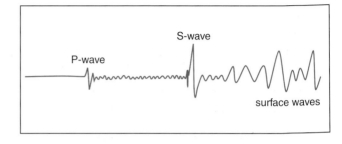

Figure E7 A typical seismogram: P-waves arrive first

The speeds of P- and S-waves depend on the density, pressure and temperature of the carrying medium. Their speeds at different depths are shown in Figure E8. Any changes in speed result in a change in wave direction, i.e. the waves refract.

Figure E9 shows that P- and S-waves are not detected all round the Earth's surface following an earthquake. There are regions of shadow where certain waves do not reach. The S-wave shadow shows that S-waves cannot pass through the Earth's centre. Since they are transverse, S-waves are unable to pass through liquids. The Earth therefore must have a molten core through which the S-waves cannot penetrate. The longitudinal P-waves do pass through this molten core but are refracted by it. Figure E9 also shows the paths taken by a number of shock waves through the mantle and core. P-waves are unable to reach AB or CD because of total internal reflection at the core/mantle interface. Surface waves can travel to all parts. The intensity of the initial shock determines how far they reach.

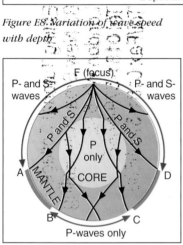

Figure E9 The shadow zones of P- and S-waves and seismic wave paths

Internal structure of the Earth

Analysis of recordings from many earthquakes, and their associated seismic wave paths, has given valuable information about the Earth's interior. The result is the layered structure shown in Figure E10.

Sudden changes in density separate the layers. The core contains 32% of the Earth's mass in only 16% of its volume. It is composed largely of iron and is the reason for the average density of the Earth being so high. The *outer core* is molten but the increasing pressure with depth produces a solid *inner*

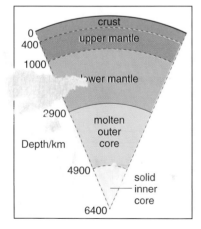

Figure E10 Internal structure of the Earth

Figu... ...fold increase in density at ... between ... ...s that temperature increases with depth, with ...

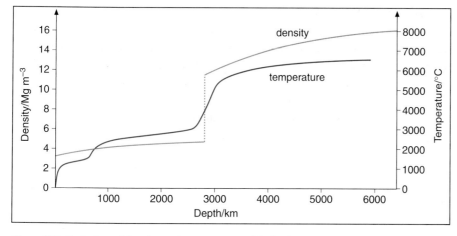

Figure E11 Variation of density and temperature with depth

Heat flow from within the Earth

Figure E11 shows the high temperature gradient, typically 25 K m^{-1}, in the Earth's crust. Heat flows out of the crust by *conduction*. Using an average value for the thermal conductivity of rock gives a rate of conduction of 4.2×10^{13} W through the crust.

If the Earth were losing energy at this rate then it would cool. If the average specific heat capacity (see Chapter 12 of *Thermal Physics*) of the Earth is 1×10^3 J kg^{-1} K^{-1}, then

$$\text{rate of cooling} = \text{rate of heat loss}/(\text{mass} \times \text{s.h.c.})$$

$$= 4.2 \times 10^{13} \text{ W}/(6 \times 10^{24} \text{ kg} \times 1 \times 10^3 \text{ J kg}^{-1} \text{ K}^{-1})$$

$$= 7 \times 10^{-15} \text{ K s}^{-1}$$

However, the Earth's surface temperature has remained more or less constant and has supported life for about 3500 million years. There must then be an *internal source of energy*.

There are two possible sources: radioactivity, and the latent heat associated with the slow solidification of the inner core. Calculations, involving the release of energy from uranium and other radioactive material in the core, show that it can only account for about 40% of the required energy. The rest must come from latent heat.

The Earth's gravity

Gravitational anomalies

Variations in the Earth's surface density result in small local variations in the g, the acceleration of free fall. Highly sensitive spring balances, called ⟨...⟩rs, are used to make relative gravity measurements. ⟨...⟩ ⟨...⟩ measure changes in g as small as ⟨...⟩. ⟨...⟩ shows the ⟨...⟩ of a *gravitational anom⟨...⟩* ⟨...⟩ ensity below the measurement site. Such a ⟨...⟩ ⟨...⟩ect the presen⟨...⟩ ⟨...⟩ bene⟨...⟩ ⟨...⟩ rock.

Ealing Tutorial College
83 New Broadway, Ealing
London W5 5AL
Tel 0181-579-6668
Tel/Fax 0181-579-8688

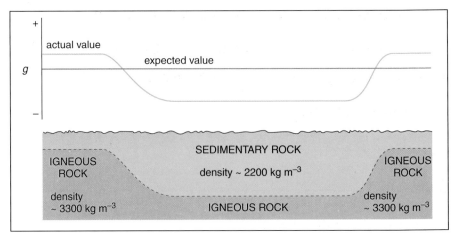

Figure E12 Gravitational anomaly

Other gravitational variations

In addition to surface density variations, other factors also have an effect on the reading of a gravimeter. Corrections have to be applied to remove these before a graph such as that shown in Figure E12 can be plotted.

The Earth is not a perfect sphere. Its radius through the poles, R_P, is less than that through the equator, R_E. A mass of 1 kg is closer to the centre of the Earth at the poles than at the equator, and therefore the value of g is greater at the poles and decreases as you move closer to the equator.

The Earth is spinning. Objects at the poles are not performing circular motion around the Earth's axis, but objects at the equator are, and need a resultant *centripetal force* on them. The magnitude of this force increases, the nearer they are to the equator. The force indicated by a balance is less than the weight by an amount equal to this centripetal force. This leads to a further lowering of the measured value of g as you get closer to the equator.

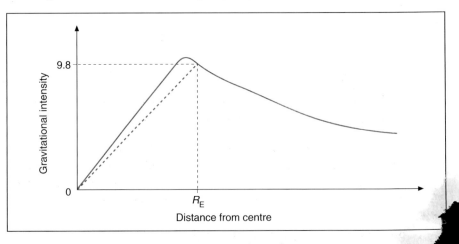

Figure E13 Variation of g below and above the Earth's surface

The dotted straight line in Figure E13 shows how g would vary *below* the surface if the Earth had a uniform density. The actual curve drawn is based on the density variations within the Earth.

Above the surface, g follows an inverse square law. At a height h:

$$g = GM/r^2 = GM/(R_E + h)^2 = GM/[R_E^2(1 + h/R_E)^2] = GM(1 + h/R_E)^{-2}/R_E^2$$

When h is small compared to R_E, it can be shown that:

$$g \approx GM(1 - 2h/R_E)/R_E^2$$

Isostasy

If you hang a pendulum next to a mountain, gravitational attraction between the mountain and the bob pulls the pendulum away from vertical. (See practice question 2.4.) However, measurements show the actual deflection to be much less than it should be. Why?

A mountain is a large rock outcrop that rises steeply above the surrounding terrain. Like an iceberg in the sea, it also extends down into the Earth. What supports this large mass of rock?

Over a short timescale, the *upper mantle* behaves like a solid. It transmits S-waves. But over a long timescale it behaves somewhat like a liquid. Heat is carried through it from core to crust by slow-moving *convection currents*. These currents move sideways when they reach the crust and are responsible for the movement of the *tectonic plates* and the drifting of the continents.

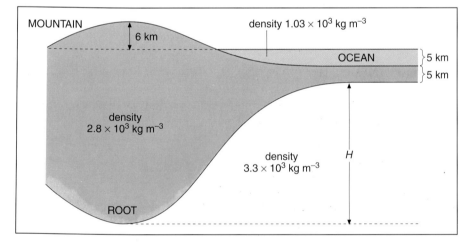

Figure E14 For equilibrium, the pressure along the dotted line is constant

The *hydrostatic pressure* (fluid pressure) in the upper mantle supports mountains and everything else on the crust. At any given level in the upper mantle, the pressure should be constant. Figure E14 shows the upper mantle supporting a section of land and sea. We can see from the equation

pressure exerted by a column = $h\rho g$

that

pressure from mountain/10^6 Pa = $(6 + 5 + 5 + H) \times 2.8 \times g$

pressure from ocean, etc./10^6 Pa = $[(5 \times 1.03) + (5 \times 2.8) + (H \times 3.3)] \times g$

For these pressures to be equal, we can work out that $H = 51.3$ km. So the *mountain's root* extends about 61 km below sea level. The pendulum bob is attracted towards the centre of the whole mountain, not simply horizontally towards that bit of the mountain above the Earth's surface.

Scandinavia is currently 'floating' at a lower level than it should be. It is still recovering from a depressed position brought about by a covering of several hundred metres of ice during the last Ice Age. It is estimated that it still has another 200 m to rise!

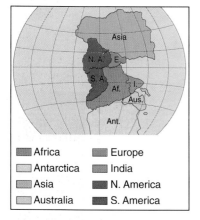

Figure E15 The continents as they were 180 million years ago

The Earth's magnetic field

If there were a powerful bar magnet positioned at the Earth's centre, it would account for the Earth's magnetic field that we now observe. The south-seeking pole of this internal magnet would have to point roughly towards geographic North to give the correct field direction. But this simple model is very unlikely. Even though the core of the Earth contains iron, its temperature is too high for it to be magnetic.

Magnetic domains (Chapter 10) are randomly orientated in an unmagnetised material and lined up in a magnet. When a magnet is heated, a temperature is reached where thermal vibrations are sufficient to destroy domain alignments. A magnet loses its magnetism at this temperature, called the *Curie temperature*. For iron, the Curie temperature (about 770 °C) is much less than the temperature within the Earth's core. So it is unlikely that the Earth's magnetic field is due to the magnetic effects of the iron.

There are a number of theories to account for the Earth's magnetic field. Massive electric currents may be circulating in the outer core, producing the magnetic field, but there is no general agreement as to how these currents are set up or maintained.

Polar wanderings and continental drift

The Earth spins about a fixed geographic axis. Over many thousands of years, the magnetic north pole is close to the Earth's North pole but the angle between the magnetic axis and the geographic axis is not fixed: it changes by about 10° every century.

As molten iron rocks cool, they solidify and remagnetise, adopting the Earth's magnetic field direction. The magnetic field direction of old rocks should give the direction of magnetic north at the time of their solidification.

When scientists first looked at magnetic alignment, rocks from different continents seemed to indicate large changes in magnetic field direction, referred to as *polar wanderings*. It is now known that these are due to continents themselves having drifted and altered direction. Turning the continent shapes until all their magnetisation directions for a particular age of rock line up shows how these originally fitted together (Figure E15).

Polar reversal and sea-floor spreading

In the centre of the Atlantic, the continental plates are moving apart. *Molten magma* wells up to solidify and create a new sea floor in the gap. It was shown in the 1960s that the mid-Atlantic sea floor has a symmetrical pattern of repeated magnetisation direction changes about its centre. This shows that the Earth's magnetic field has *reversed polarity* many times during geological history (Figure E16). The polarity does not suddenly change; its magnetic strength gradually decreases to zero and then increases in the opposite direction.

The atmosphere

Pressure variation

Atmospheric pressure is caused by the weight of air above. In Chapter 4 of *Thermal Physics* we calculated a height of 8 km for an atmosphere of uniform density. In such an atmosphere, pressure would decrease linearly with height. However, air density decreases with height. In an *isothermal* (constant-temperature) atmosphere, pressure decreases exponentially with height:

$$p = p_0\, e^{-kh} \qquad \text{where} \qquad k = 1.14 \times 10^{-4}\ \text{m}^{-1}$$

Figure E17 shows this variation.

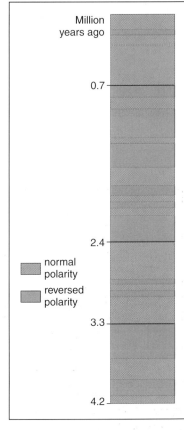

Figure E16 Significant changes in polarity over the last 4.2 million years

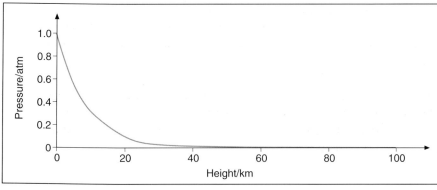

Figure E17 Pressure variation with height in an isothermal atmosphere

Use the equation to show that the pressure in an isothermal atmosphere would halve every 6 km [= (ln 2)/(1.14 × 10⁻⁴ m⁻¹)]. Although the atmosphere is well over 100 km high, 50% of its mass is within the first 6 km. Above 60 km, the pressure drops to below one-thousandth of its surface value, far too small to show up on the graph.

The four principal atmospheric layers

The atmosphere can be divided into four distinct layers: *troposphere*, *stratosphere*, *mesosphere* and *thermosphere*. The troposphere contains about 80% of the atmosphere's mass. It holds the key to the world's weather and climate. The four layers are shown in Figure E18, together with the temperature variations within them. *Temperature gradient* reverses from one layer to the next.

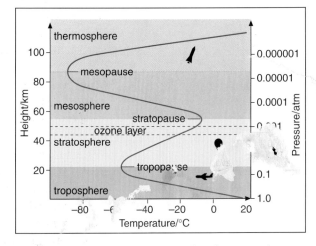

Figure E18 Temperature variation within the principal atmospheric layers

Explaining the temperature variations

The lower atmosphere is mainly heated from below. The Earth's surface absorbs incoming solar radiation and emits infra-red into the atmosphere. Carbon dioxide and water vapour in the troposphere absorb this infra-red. Most absorption occurs lower down. Temperature falls as height increases at a steady rate of 6.5 K km^{-1} (the lapse rate).

The stratosphere's temperature increases with height. It is warmed by the absorption of ultra-violet by ozone (O_3). In this way the *ozone layer* prevents harmful ultra-violet reaching the Earth's surface. It is important that this layer is maintained and not depleted by the chemicals we use. *CFCs* (chlorofluorocarbons) destroy ozone. In the past, they were used widely as aerosol propellants and in refrigerators, but their use is now restricted.

No absorption occurs in the mesosphere and therefore its temperature decreases with height. The thermosphere is warmed by absorption of short-wavelength ultra-violet by atomic and molecular oxygen.

Escaping the atmosphere

Chapter 5 shows that an upward speed of 11 km s^{-1} is required to escape the Earth. At 300 K, hydrogen atoms have an r.m.s. speed of 3 km s^{-1}. They would appear to be trapped. The kinetic theory of gases points to a distribution of speeds (Chapter 8 of *Thermal Physics*). A very small fraction of hydrogen, and also helium, atoms will have sufficient speed to escape. Over a very long timescale (the age of the Earth), these two light gases have leaked away and their amounts in the atmosphere are very low. Only the heavier gases remain trapped.

Emitted radiation

A hot body emits a wide range of *electromagnetic wavelengths* (Figure E19). A white-hot object emits a greater proportion of shorter wavelengths than a red-hot object.

The wavelength at which the emitted intensity peaks (λ_{max}) decreases with increasing temperature of the body. *Wien's displacement law* states that λ_{max} is inversely proportional to absolute temperature T:

$$\lambda_{max} \propto 1/T \qquad \text{or} \qquad \lambda_{max}T = \text{constant} = 2.898 \times 10^{-3} \text{ m K}$$

The total power emitted, E, is the area under the curve. *Stefan's law* states that this is proportional to the fourth power of the body's absolute temperature T. It also depends on its surface area A:

$$E = \sigma A T^4 \qquad \text{where Stefan's constant } \sigma = 5.67 \times 10^{-8} \text{ W m}^{-2} \text{ K}^{-4}.$$

Energy from the Sun

The Sun has a surface temperature of 5800 K and a radius of 7.0×10^8 m. Use Stefan's law to show that the total power emitted is 4.0×10^{26} W. This power spreads uniformly into space, and some of it, after travelling 1.5×10^{11} m, falls

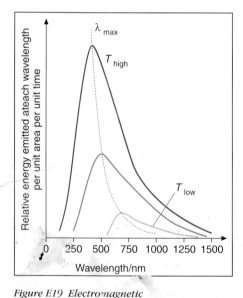

Figure E19 Electromagnetic wavelengths emitted by a hot body

Meteosat and NOAA

Table E3 lists wavelengths used by Meteosat and NOAA satellites.

Table E3 *Scanning wavelength ranges (μm)*

Region of EM spectrum	Possible use	Wavelengths used/μm	
		Meteosat	**NOAA**
visible window	cloud formations	0.4–...	0.58–0.68
near-infra-red window	vegetation monitoring	...–1.1	0.73–1.10 3.55–3.93
reflected by water vapour	rain-bearing clouds	5.7–7.1	
thermal infra-red window	ground and sea-surface temperatures	10.5–12.5	10.3–11.3 11.5–12.5

Geostationary satellites orbit above the equator. Five suitably positioned geostationary satellites (72° separation) would survey the equator and everything between latitudes ±55° superbly. But they would be looking at the Earth's surface obliquely for latitudes above and below ±55°. Their coverage of the UK is poor and is supplemented with daily images from NOAA.

Landsat programme

The American *Landsat* satellites investigate soil characteristics, crop size, coastal-water pollution and the health of forests. They need high resolution, e.g. 30 m, requiring an impossible image frequency of 5 MHz. Rather than reduce the strip width, Landsat satellites use six separate scanners, each operating at less than 1 MHz. They take 16 days to cover the whole of the Earth's surface.

Landsat-1 was launched in 1972. It used a *multispectral optical scanner* in addition to television cameras. Landsat-5 scanning involves the use of seven different wavelength ranges.

Radar sensors

The principle of *radar* is to send out short bursts of electromagnetic waves and record those that return. Radar sensors can collect information through clouds. An aerial transmits signal bursts both sideways and straight down. It then receives the reflected signals. Computer software applies *Doppler theory* to the returning signals to build up a picture.

The longer the aerial, the greater its resolution. *Synthetic Aperture Radar* uses the motion of the satellite to make its aerial appear longer. It stores information received over a long length of path, and processes this information as though it came from an aerial as big as the path from which the information is collected. This means that the picture it produces is very detailed. Synthetic Aperture Radar is used extensively in the European Satellite ERS-1 shown in Figure E29.

Figure E29 ERS-1 contains an Along Track Scanning Radiometer. Microwave sensors measure atmospheric water vapour levels and infra-red sensors measure sea-surface temperatures

Particle Physics Topic

Probing the nucleus

Inside the atom

The *Rutherford scattering* experiment, described in Chapter 7 of *Matter and Waves*, showed that atoms have a tiny positively charged central *nucleus* surrounded by a cloud of negatively charged *electrons*. In the experiment, each alpha particle had a kinetic energy of about 1.23×10^{-12} J and a charge of 3.20×10^{-19} C. Gold nuclei have a charge of 127×10^{-19} C. When an alpha particle travels directly towards a nucleus, they repel each other. Kinetic energy is lost as electrostatic potential energy is gained. At the instant the particle reverses direction:

$$\text{initial kinetic energy} = \text{electrostatic potential energy}$$

$$1.23 \times 10^{-12} \text{ J} = (3.20 \times 10^{-19} \text{ C} \times 127 \times 10^{-19} \text{ C})/(4\pi\varepsilon_0 r)$$

where r is the distance between the centres of the two charges. This gives an estimate for r of the order of 10^{-14} m. The nucleus must be smaller than this, and so its *protons* and *neutrons* must have diameters of the order of 10^{-15} m (Table P1).

Protons have a charge of 1.60×10^{-19} C. Within the nucleus they experience repulsion F from other protons about 10^{-15} m away:

$$F = (1.60 \times 10^{-19} \text{ C} \times 1.60 \times 10^{-19} \text{ C})/[4\pi\varepsilon_0(1 \times 10^{-15} \text{ m})^2] = 230 \text{ N}$$

This is a huge force on the atomic scale. But it does not make the protons in the nucleus fly apart, so there must be a very strong force holding them together. This attractive force must act over a *very short range* because, during alpha scattering, it does not attract and capture the protons in an alpha particle.

Smashing atoms

If we want to examine things, we look at them. But for very small objects light is useless, because its wavelength is too big. You can see from Table P1 that the size of the nucleus is much smaller than the wavelength of light. If you want to examine the structure of the nucleus, you need something with a very short wavelength.

Firing alpha particles at atoms provided evidence for the nucleus. It is an example of the particle physicist's standard tool: investigating the structure of matter by firing particles at it. You know from Chapter 31 of *Matter and Waves* that a particle has a wavelength λ related to its momentum p by the *de Broglie*

Table P1 *The nuclear scale – each step is ten times smaller than the one before*

1 m	child's height
10^{-1} m	
10^{-2} m	finger nail length
10^{-3} m	
10^{-4} m	hair thickness
10^{-5} m	
10^{-6} m	light wavelength
10^{-7} m	
10^{-8} m	smallest virus
10^{-9} m	
10^{-10} m	atomic diameter
10^{-11} m	
10^{-12} m	
10^{-13} m	
10^{-14} m	nucleus
10^{-15} m	nucleon

relationship, $\lambda = h/p$, where h is the Planck constant. Fast-moving particles have a very short wavelength. Firing them at matter is like investigating that matter with very short wavelengths. An electron with energy 6 GeV has a wavelength of 2.1×10^{-16} m. So it can reveal objects in the nucleus.

Figure P1 shows a *linear accelerator* or *linac*, which accelerates charged particles along an evacuated tube. It has a straight tube and a series of charged plates. The voltage between the plates switches from positive to negative repeatedly. This continually accelerates those particles which travel through the holes from one stage to another when the voltage switches (Figure P2).

The particles in the accelerator beam must be readily available and stable. They are usually electrons or protons. Electrons were used initially because they are easy to produce in large numbers, easy to accelerate because of their low mass, and have relatively simple interactions.

The beams are directed at a *target*, usually a tank of liquid hydrogen. The beam collides with the fixed protons – the hydrogen nuclei.

Creating new particles

When the particles in a beam collide with the target, they lose energy. Some of this energy is given to the target. But, in some collisions, some of the energy is used to create new particles.

When a beam collides with a fixed target, the products of the collision have a total momentum equal to the initial momentum of the accelerated particle. This is not, of course, zero. Therefore, the collision products have kinetic energy, and therefore not all the energy of the accelerated particle can be used to create new particles.

If the accelerating tube is a ring (Figure P3), the particles can be accelerated for very much longer periods and so gain much more momentum. Large magnets deflect the accelerated particles from a straight line into a circular path (Figure P4). Particles with opposite charges can be accelerated in opposite directions at the same time; they cross in chambers where the collision products can be tracked.

Figure P1 The Stanford linear accelerator is 3 km long and can accelerate electrons to 50 GeV

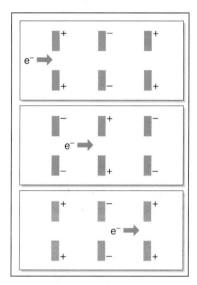

Figure P2 The principle of the linear accelerator

Figure P3 The large ring at CERN in Geneva has a circumference of 27 km and has more than 4000 magnets to control and steer the beam of particles

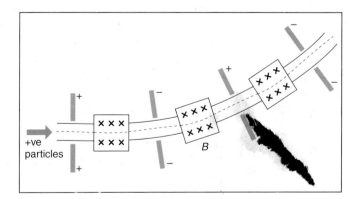

Figure P4 The principle of the ring accelerator

PARTICLE PHYSICS TOPIC

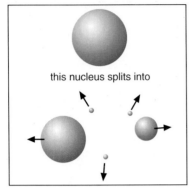

Figure P5 *If the original nucleus was at rest, the total final momentum must also be zero*

When they collide, the initial momenta are usually equal and opposite, so the products can in principle have zero momentum and therefore zero kinetic energy. So all the available energy can be used to create new particles. Collisions are more likely between a beam and a dense fixed target than between two beams, but in modern rings the beams can be steered very precisely and can be made to cross and collide very many times each second.

If a particle at rest decays into two or more products, their total final momentum must be zero. Figure P5 shows a uranium nucleus splitting up into a number of fission fragments. The total final momentum in both the X and the Y directions must be zero.

Particle detectors

Charged particles *ionise* the atoms of liquid or gas through which they pass. The number of ions produced depends on charge and velocity. A *bubble chamber* is filled with liquid hydrogen and charged particles passing through leave a trail of ions, around which small bubbles form. Photographs taken from different angles show the precise track of each particle (Figure P6).

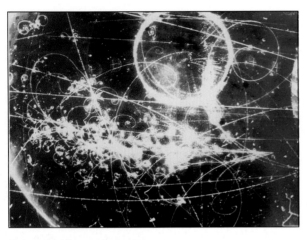

Figure P6 *A beam of neutrinos (invisible in the picture) entered this bubble chamber and one collision produced this dramatic spray of particles*

Spark chambers (Figure P7) and *drift chambers* have plates or wires carrying high potentials, so, when particles ionise the gas in the chamber, a current flows between the plates or wires. A computer can quickly reconstruct the paths of the particles and select events that show particular features.

Most charged particles have a charge equal or opposite to the electronic charge, so in a known magnetic field the direction and radius of curvature of the tracks give a direct indication of the charge and momentum of the particles (Figure P8). Other features allow other properties to be found. A particle with no charge leaves no track but can be detected by a gap or kink in other tracks.

Analysing particle collisions

Physicists take measurements of momentum and kinetic energy of the particles involved, before and after they collide. As you know from Chapter 15, for a charged particle moving at right angles to a magnetic field:

$$mv^2/r = Bqv \quad \text{so} \quad mv = Bqr$$

The momentum $p = mv$. It is proportional to the radius of the path (Figure P9). Positive particles curve one way, negative the other.

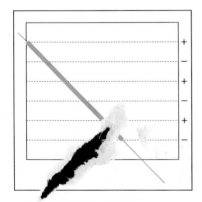

Figure P7 *A spark chamber*

Third-generation particles

In 1975 an even more massive lepton was discovered, matched by another massive quark in 1977. This suggested a third generation of massive particles and antiparticles, called the *tau* τ⁻, *tau neutrino* v_τ, and *top* and *bottom* quarks (t and b). The very massive top quark was confirmed in 1996 (Table P7).

Theoretical and experimental results indicate that there are no more generations, but cannot yet explain why there are three, or why the particles within them have the masses they do.

Table P7 *The third-generation*

Leptons		Quarks	
$\bar{v}_\tau$	v_τ	t	$\bar{t}$
0.0 GeV/c² *		180 GeV/c²	
τ⁺	τ⁻	b	$\bar{b}$
1./8 GeV/c²		4.58 GeV/c²	

*Neutrinos may have a small but negligible mass

Hadrons

Quarks never occur alone. They *always* occur in combinations of two or three, forming the hadrons. There are three types of hadrons (Table P8): *mesons* have one quark and one antiquark ($q\bar{q}$); *baryons* have three quarks (qqq); *antibaryons* have three antiquarks ($\bar{q}\bar{q}\bar{q}$).

Table P8 *Examples of hadrons*

Mesons	Symbol	$q\bar{q}$	Charge
pi minus	π⁻	$d\bar{u}$	−1
eta zero	η⁰	$s\bar{s}$	0
D plus	D⁺	$c\bar{d}$	+1
Baryons	**Symbol**	**qqq**	**Charge**
delta double plus	Δ⁺⁺	uuu	+2
proton	p	uud	+1
neutron	n	udd	0
omega minus	Ω⁻	sss	−1
Antibaryons	**Symbol**	**$\bar{q}\bar{q}\bar{q}$**	**Charge**
antiproton	$\bar{p}$	$\bar{u}\bar{u}\bar{d}$	−1
antilambda	$\bar{\Lambda}$	$\bar{u}\bar{d}\bar{s}$	0

The masses of the hadrons are known from observations. But these cannot be used to find precise masses for the quarks they contain because energy is released when quarks bind together, in the same way that *binding energy* is released when nucleons form nuclei (Chapter 9 of *Matter and Waves*). Hadrons have less mass than the separate quarks, but the size of the binding energy is unknown. In addition, some mesons and baryons can exist in excited states that appear to be more massive than usual.

Only four mesons, called π mesons (pions), can be made from the first generation of quarks: $d\bar{u}$, $d\bar{d}$, $u\bar{u}$ and $u\bar{d}$. Adding s and $\bar{s}$ allows the formation of another five mesons (Table P9).

Pions occur commonly in particle collisions because they contain the quarks with the lowest masses and so are produced more easily than more massive particles. The second- and third-generation quarks and antiquarks make mesons in the same way, with the same pattern of charges. But these more massive mesons are observed less frequently, if at all, in collisions. Mesons can also be formed by quarks from different generations, giving 36 possibilities.

For example, a u$\bar{\text{b}}$ meson has charges of $+\frac{2}{3}$ and $+\frac{1}{3}$, making an overall charge of $+1$. Particles containing a strange or charm quark (s, $\bar{\text{s}}$, or c, $\bar{\text{c}}$) are often called strange or charmed particles, but apart from their mass they behave like those with u or d quarks.

Table P9 *The nine mesons (light backgrounds) made from u, d and s quarks and antiquarks (dark-blue backgrounds), showing their charge and mass*

Quarks	Antiquarks		
	$\bar{\text{d}} \quad +\frac{1}{3}$	$\bar{\text{u}} \quad -\frac{2}{3}$	$\bar{\text{s}} \quad +\frac{1}{3}$
d $\quad -\frac{1}{3}$	d$\bar{\text{d}} \quad \pi^0$ 0.135 GeV/c^2	d$\bar{\text{u}} \quad \pi^-$ 0.140 GeV/c^2	d$\bar{\text{s}} \quad$ K^0 0.498 GeV/c^2
u $\quad +\frac{2}{3}$	u$\bar{\text{d}} \quad \pi^+$ 0.140 GeV/c^2	u$\bar{\text{u}} \quad \pi^0$ 0.135 GeV/c^2	u$\bar{\text{s}} \quad$ K$^+$ 0.494 GeV/c^2
s $\quad -\frac{1}{3}$	s$\bar{\text{d}} \quad$ K^0 0.498 GeV/c^2	s$\bar{\text{u}} \quad$ K$^-$ 0.494 GeV/c^2	s$\bar{\text{s}} \quad \eta^0$ 0.958 GeV/c^2

You could also draw up tables of baryons (qqq) or antibaryons ($\bar{\text{q}}\bar{\text{q}}\bar{\text{q}}$), giving well over 200 possibilities. Only two are important: the proton and neutron, which contain u and d quarks from the first generation. The proton has a charge of $+1$, so must have two charges of $+\frac{2}{3}$ and one charge of $-\frac{1}{3}$; two u quarks and one d quark (Table P8). The neutron is neutral and can only be made from one charge of $+\frac{2}{3}$ and two charges of $-\frac{1}{3}$; one u and two d quarks.

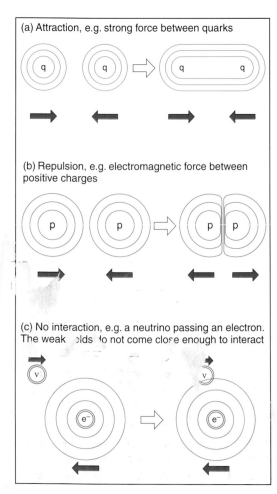

(a) Attraction, e.g. strong force between quarks

(b) Repulsion, e.g. electromagnetic force between positive charges

(c) No interaction, e.g. a neutrino passing an electron. The weak fields do not come close enough to interact

Figure P13 Particle interactions represented as fields

Fundamental forces

Leptons and quarks interact (influence each other) in four different ways, called the *weak*, *electromagnetic*, *strong* and *gravitational* interactions. These only occur because of the fundamental properties of each type of particle, such as its mass or charge. They do not depend on any external field or force (Table P10).

In an interaction the particles are either attracted towards or repelled away from each other. Imagine that each particle and hadron is surrounded by a tiny field for each interaction in which it takes part.

Any quark has all four fields whereas a neutrino is thought to have only one, the weak field. Particles interact only if they come close enough together for similar fields to overlap. If the field lines merge around both particles, they are pulled together; but if the lines do not merge, the particles are pushed apart (Figure P13). These tiny pulls or pushes between particles are the origin of all the forces between large objects.

Table P10 *The interactions felt by leptons and quarks*

Interaction	Leptons		Quarks
	Neutrinos	Charged leptons	
weak	✓	✓	✓
electromagnetic		✓	✓
strong			✓
gravitational	?	✓	✓

Exchange particles

During interactions the energy associated with the field that causes the interaction can change. Sometimes the energy of the field decreases and another particle is formed. Sometimes a particle disappears and the energy of the field increases. So the number and type of particles present can change. On this scale, energy can only be exchanged in fixed amounts called *quanta*, just as light energy is packaged into quanta or particles called photons. The quanta are called *exchange particles* to distinguish them from matter particles, and each field has its own type of exchange particle (Table P11).

Table P11 *Exchange particles*

Interaction	Name and symbol	Mass	Range	Typical decay times
weak	W^+, W^-, Z^0	~90 GeV/c^2	well within hadron	10^{-10} s
electromagnetic	photon γ	0	infinite	10^{-18} s
strong	gluon g	0	within hadron	10^{-23} s
gravitational	graviton *g*	0	infinite	–

Interactions occur when particles come close enough for a quantum of energy to form and for an exchange to take place. The weak field is limited to about 10^{-18} m, well within the diameter of a hadron. In effect, the particles have to be in contact before this interaction can occur. The very short range is explained by the high mass of the W^+, W^- and Z^0 exchange particles. They require a lot of energy for their production and they decay very quickly into particles with lower mass. They have only a very short time and range in which to act.

Rutherford scattering shows that the electromagnetic field has a much greater range than the weak field or the strong field. Photons have no mass and so are easy to produce, and charged particles usually interact electromagnetically before the other fields are able to interact. Gluons also have zero mass but have a short range because they themselves feel the strong field and cannot separate from quarks. The masses of individual particles are so small that gravitational interactions can be ignored. Mass nevertheless plays an important part in determining how the other three fields interact and exchange energy.

Conservation laws

Interactions are related to the mass, charge and generation of particles (Figure P14). They obey specific *conservation laws*.

Mass–energy always has the same value before and after an interaction. Momentum and charge Q are also always conserved. The number of leptons L is also conserved. The appearance or disappearance of each lepton particle ($L = +1$) is always balanced by the appearance or disappearance of a lepton antiparticle ($L = -1$), even within each lepton generation.

The number of quarks is conserved, but quarks can be counted only in mesons ($q\bar{q}$) and baryons (qqq and $\bar{q}\,\bar{q}\,\bar{q}$). Mesons already balance a quark with an antiquark, and so can appear or disappear in interactions and are not

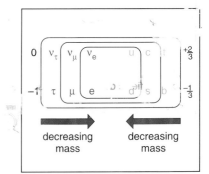

Figure P14 The three generations of particles and their charges. Antiparticles have the opposite charge

Mesons with zero charge can materialise at energies appropriate to their masses. The π^0 appears at energies above 0.135 GeV, $s\bar{s}$ at 0.958 GeV, $c\bar{c}$ at about 3 GeV and $b\bar{b}$ at about 10 GeV. Like all mesons, these are unstable and the quark and antiquark annihilate into photons. Charged mesons cannot annihilate in this way because charge must be conserved and cannot be carried by neutral photons; decay has to involve a W^+ or W^- and so takes longer than electromagnetic decay, as it takes time for the exchange particle to form.

Annihilations of p and $\bar{p}$ give similar pair production, but because the rest-mass energy is so much higher, the number of pairs or the masses of the particles can be correspondingly greater.

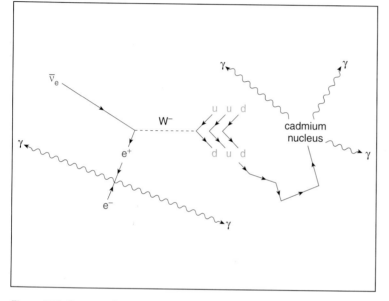

Figure P19 *Capture of an energetic neutrino*

Detecting neutrinos

Neutrinos can only interact with other particles if they collide with sufficient energy to form a W or Z exchange particle. In principle, neutrinos might be detected by making beta decay go backwards, turning a proton into a neutron. But it is impossible to imagine how to make the $\bar{\nu}_e$, e^- and u quark collide at the same instant to make a d quark (Figure P15a). However, the weak interaction actually changes leptons and quarks from one type to another, and the Feynman diagram suggests a different mechanism for detecting neutrinos. An incoming $\bar{\nu}_e$ could interact with a u quark in a proton and change to a e^+ as the u changes to a d quark (Figure P19). Q, L and B are all conserved.

A suitable experiment could be designed only when the decays of the fission fragments in nuclear reactors created very large numbers of neutrinos. A large tank of cadmium chloride solution was surrounded by 90 light detectors. Every few minutes a $\bar{\nu}_e$ interacted with a u quark in the proton of a water molecule. The e^+ immediately annihilated with an e^- into a pair of photons, which travelled in opposite directions (conservation of momentum) and therefore caused flashes on opposite sides of the tank. The resulting neutron was free to scatter off other nuclei until it could be absorbed by one of the cadmium nuclei. This then emitted a burst of gamma rays to get rid of the excess energy. So two opposing flashes followed quickly by a burst of photons was very good evidence that $\bar{\nu}_e$ capture had occurred, especially as the frequency of the events could be related directly to the activity of the reactor core.

Strong interactions (gluon exchange)

Strong interactions are short-range attractions between all of the quarks and antiquarks. Leptons and antileptons are never involved. Quarks and antiquarks are strongly bound into mesons and baryons, from which they cannot separate, whereas the leptons are always observed as separate particles. Protons and neutrons are less strongly bound together in the nucleus by the residual effects of gluon exchange within the baryons themselves.

The attraction between quarks can be represented by a Feynman diagram, but it is more interesting to look at interactions between the hadrons (Figure P20). Colliding protons may just scatter electromagnetically, but at higher energy new particles such as a π^0 (d$\bar{\text{d}}$) meson may materialise.

This and other strong interactions can be explained by imagining that a quark is displaced from one of the colliding protons. As it moves away from the others, the gluons have to travel over a longer distance. Unlike photons, the gluons themselves interact with the field, and at a range of about 10^{-15} m they materialise into a q$\bar{\text{q}}$ pair. All of the quarks then recombine into baryons and mesons.

If a charged meson appears, charge is conserved because one proton is replaced by a baryon with zero charge such as a neutron (Figure P20c). As before, a d and $\bar{\text{d}}$ pair has materialised, but the quarks have combined in a different way, u$\bar{\text{d}}$ and dud instead of d$\bar{\text{d}}$ and uud. At even higher energy it is possible for more massive quarks from other generations to materialise (Figure P20d). Check that Q, B and S are conserved. Strangeness and charm are always conserved in strong interactions because the quarks materialise in q$\bar{\text{q}}$ pairs.

At very high energies more than one quark might be knocked a very long way from the others and a string of q$\bar{\text{q}}$ pairs can materialise along its path. These may combine to form various baryons, antibaryons and mesons. Some pairs might annihilate, but since quarks are always materialised or annihilated in pairs of similar type, the overall number of quarks of each type is always conserved in strong interactions.

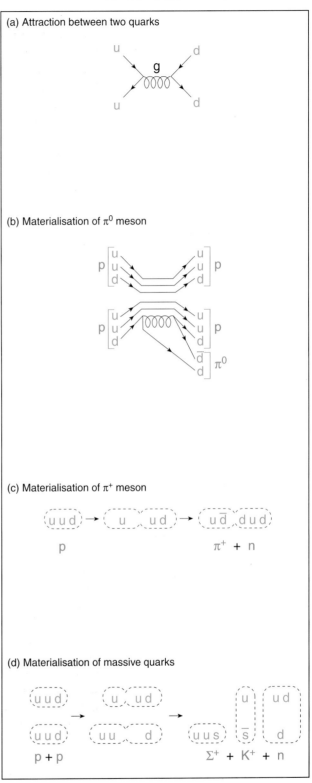

(a) Attraction between two quarks

(b) Materialisation of π^0 meson

(c) Materialisation of π^+ meson

(d) Materialisation of massive quarks

Figure P20 Strong interactions

Grand unification theories

The Z^0 acts on all particles and the photon only on charged particles, but otherwise they have very similar effects in some interactions. In mathematical terms they appear to be alternative versions of the same particle, one with mass and one without. This has led to the idea that at very high energies it might also be possible to consider the gluon and maybe the graviton to be alternative versions of these particles, so leading to the idea of a single underlying field that would account for all known interactions and forces between matter.

The nature of the universe

You can use a prism to disperse light from nearby stars and galaxies into a spectrum. Narrow dark bands occur at particular wavelengths because atoms in the outer layer of each star absorb photons of these wavelengths. These bands exactly match those for hydrogen and helium atoms. Their relative widths suggest that most of the matter in the universe is hydrogen and helium atoms, in a ratio of about 3:1 by mass (Figure P21).

If a light source and an observer move with the same velocity, the wavelength of the light leaving the source has the same wavelength when it arrives at the observer. But if the source is moving away, then each wave is slightly longer when it reaches the observer, because the source moves slightly by the time the next wave is emitted. The light appears to be shifted towards a longer (redder) wavelength (Figure P22).

The faster the speed of the source, the greater the *red-shift*. Absorption bands in the spectra of distant galaxies appear to be shifted towards the red end of the spectrum (Figure P23). This suggests that distant galaxies are moving away from us.

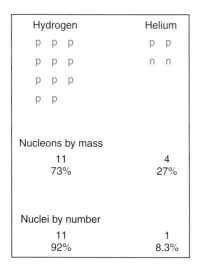

Figure P21 *Ratio of hydrogen to helium in the universe*

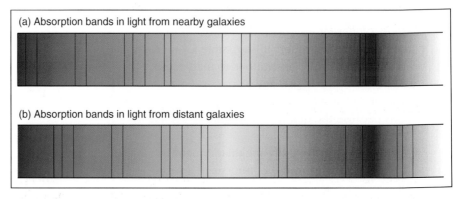

Figure P23 *Red-shift of light from distant galaxies*

The theory of relativity suggests that space itself is expanding and is stretching the light waves from distant galaxies whilst they are travelling. The bands for hydrogen and helium still give a reference for the extent of the shift and hence the apparent speed of a galaxy. In 1929 Edwin Hubble observed that the shift speed z is proportional to the distance d of the galaxy, and that more distant galaxies seem to be moving away from us more quickly:

$$z = Hd \quad \text{Hubble's law}$$

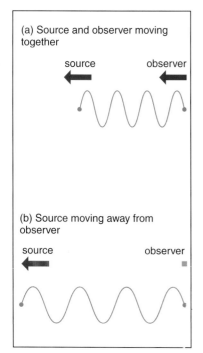

Figure P22 *Red-shift and wavelength of light*

where H is the Hubble constant. It is very difficult to measure d precisely, but galaxies at about 9.5×10^{21} km seem to be moving away at typical speeds of about 1.5×10^{4} km s^{-1}. This gives an estimate for H of 1.8×10^{-18} s^{-1}, so z only becomes significant if d is very large.

The origin of the universe

All distant galaxies seem to be travelling away from us. If this process has been continuing for some time, the galaxies must once have been much closer, and matter must once have been packed together into a very small volume.

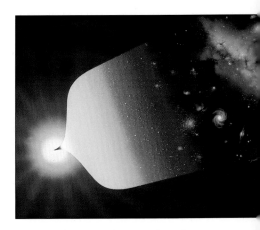

Figure P24 An artist's impression of the history of the universe

Dividing the distance of a galaxy from us by its speed of travel away from us gives an estimate for the time taken for the expansion: in the above case, this gives about 15×10^{9} years.

If the universe has expanded from a small volume, gravitational forces will tend to pull it back together. Its potential energy increases; its kinetic energy and the random kinetic energy of its parts decreases. So the temperature has decreased down to its present average of about 3 K. It must once have been hotter.

These ideas led to the theory that the universe began with a very dense hot '*Big Bang*' about 15×10^{9} years ago, and has been cooling down ever since. Figure P24 shows an artist's impression of the history of the universe.

The quark–lepton era

If our scientific models are correct, the very early universe was unimaginably dense and hot, and our ideas of temperature, space and time probably did not apply. Free particles and antiparticles, separate leptons and quarks, had very high kinetic energies and constantly materialised from exchange particles and instantly annihilated. As the particles began to disperse, their kinetic energies fell and the rematerialisation of massive particles became less and less likely. The decay of the massive exchange particles produced a small excess of matter particles over antiparticles, which eventually remained to form the present universe.

The hadron era: 10^{13} K, 7×10^{-7} s onwards

Gluons began to bind quarks and antiquarks into mesons ($q\bar{q}$) and baryons (qqq and $\bar{q}\bar{q}\bar{q}$). These free hadrons decayed and also annihilated each other, but existed for longer periods as the universe expanded and cooled. Materialisations became less likely as photons no longer had sufficient energy to convert into mass. Neutrons (n and $\bar{n}$) and especially protons (p and $\bar{p}$) had the least mass and were most likely to form and could not easily decay. Annihilations left a small excess of quarks (q), which formed about 12 protons for every three neutrons. By about 3 s, at 10^9 K, electron pairs could no longer materialise and annihilations left a small excess of free electrons. The universe was a plasma of very energetic protons, neutrons, electrons and photons, all scattering off each other electromagnetically, plus freely moving neutrinos. Some neutrons still changed into protons by the weak β^- decay process.

Nucleus formation: about 200 s onwards

There were about 13 protons for every two neutrons. They began to bind together as pn pairs as they were no longer knocked apart by collisions with other particles. This stopped further beta decay of these neutrons. The pn pairs also began to form helium nuclei, which are very stable, leaving 11 protons for every one helium nucleus, as observed in the universe today (Figure P21). By the time stable larger nuclei might have been able to form, all the neutrons were already combined into helium nuclei.

The atomic era: 3×10^3 K, 300 000 years onwards

Instead of scattering off the protons and nuclei, free electrons began to bind to them electromagnetically, forming stable atoms. These could not be ionised by the remaining photons, which could now travel freely through space. Since then the universe has gone on expanding by about 10^9 times (1000 times along each linear dimension). The wavelength of the photons has also stretched by about 1000 times, so the temperature they represent has dropped from 3×10^3 K to about 3 K, the background temperature of the present universe. Atoms have zero electric charge, so the nuclei no longer felt electrostatic repulsion. Atoms could begin to group together under the influence of gravitational attraction, and go on to form stars and galaxies.

The end of the universe

The masses of the galaxies attract each other gravitationally, so the rate of expansion of the universe is probably slowly decreasing. If there is enough mass in the universe, the universe is *closed*: it will stop and begin to collapse back towards a single point. If the mass is insufficient for that to happen, the universe is *open*: it will go on expanding for ever but at a slower and slower rate (Figure P25).

For collapse to occur, the average density of the universe would have to be about 1×10^{-26} kg m^{-3}, or about six atoms per metre cubed of space. Visible matter accounts for only 2–3% of this critical value. However, the observed movements of galaxies cannot be explained simply in terms of the gravitational attractions between the masses of the visible matter that they contain. The forces seem to be much stronger, suggesting that there is a lot of dark matter (not stars) exerting gravitational attraction and placing the average density of the universe much closer to the critical density.

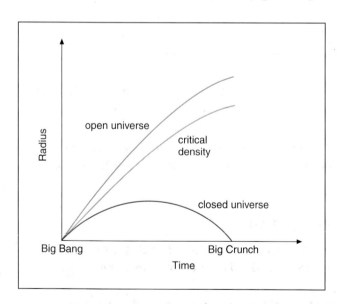

Figure P25 *Depending on its density, the universe may expand for ever, or contract back to a 'Big Crunch'*

Practice questions

Chapter 1

1.1 Distinguish between the terms *mass* and *weight*.

1.2 What is a gravitational field? Define *gravitational field strength*.

1.3 Show that the units of gravitational field strength are equivalent to those of acceleration. Use the data in the chapter to find the acceleration of the Moon due to the attraction between it and the Earth.

Chapter 2

2.1 State Newton's law of gravitation. Show that the unit of the universal gravitational constant is N m² kg⁻². Express this in base units.

2.2 The density of lead is 11400 kg m⁻³. Calculate the radius of a lead sphere that has a mass of 6 kg. Calculate the gravitational force of attraction between two of these spheres when they are touching.

2.3 A 75 g mass is placed midway between a 300 g mass and a 500 g mass that are 40 cm apart. Find the magnitude and direction of the resultant gravitational force acting on it.

2.4 One method for measuring the universal gravitational constant *G* involves mounting a simple pendulum from a rigid support close to the side of a mountain. Gravitational attraction between the pendulum bob and the mountain pulls the pendulum away from the vertical as shown in the diagram. A suitable mountain for this experiment (and a very good climb!) is Schiehallion in Scotland. Draw a free-body force diagram to show the forces acting on the pendulum bob. Approximately, the volume of Schiehallion is 1.6 × 10⁹ m³ and its density is 3000 kg m⁻³. Calculate the gravitational force it would exert on a 2 kg pendulum bob placed as shown in the diagram. Calculate the angle from the vertical through which the pendulum would be deflected.

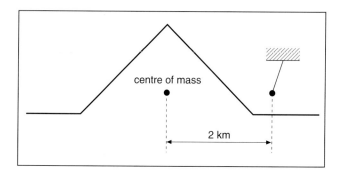

2.5 Question 2.4 assumes that the centres of mass of the bob and the mountain are horizontally aligned. In practice, the mountain's centre of mass is much lower. Discuss the effect that this will have on the angle through which the pendulum is deflected.

Chapter 3

3.1 Explain why, although a satellite is in free fall, it remains the same distance above the Earth. Why is its speed unaffected by the gravitational force acting on it?

3.2 Given that the Earth's orbital radius is 1.5 × 10¹¹ m, use the values in Table 3.1 to plot a graph of (period/s)² against (radius of orbit/m)³ for the planets. Use the gradient of your graph to determine the mass of the Sun.

3.3 Calculate the period of a near-Earth satellite, one where *g* ≈ 9.8 N kg⁻¹ and orbital radius *r* ≈ 6400 km.

3.4 What is a *geostationary satellite*? Calculate the height of such a satellite above the Earth's surface.

Chapter 4

4.1 The Earth's gravitational field obeys an inverse square law. What is meant by *inverse square law*?

4.2 A satellite orbits the Earth (radius 6.4 Mm) at a height of 9.6 Mm above the surface. Find the ratio between the two radii. The acceleration due to

PRACTICE QUESTIONS

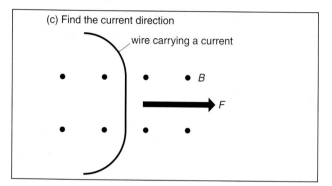

(c) Find the current direction

wire carrying a current

B

F

12.3 Describe how you would show that the force exerted on a conductor carrying current in a magnetic field is proportional to the current flowing.

Chapter 13

13.1 Define the *tesla*. Express the tesla in base units.

13.2 Describe how a digital balance can be used to measure the strength of a uniform magnetic field.

13.3 The speech coil in a small loudspeaker has a diameter of 4 cm and consists of 300 turns. The speaker magnet produces a radial magnetic field that is always perpendicular to this coil. If the magnetic field strength is 200 mT, calculate the force on the coil when it carries a current of 5 mA. Explain what happens to the speech coil when an alternating current flows in it.

13.4 The diagram shows a rigid wire loop connected to a 6.0 V battery and a 6.0 V, 9.0 W lamp.

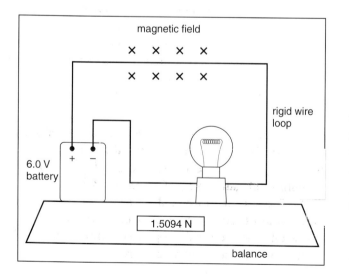

magnetic field

× × × ×

× × × ×

rigid wire loop

6.0 V battery

1.5094 N

balance

The circuit is standing on a top-pan electronic balance. A uniform horizontal magnetic field, strength 50 mT, acts at right angles to 100 mm of the straight top part of the wire. The reading on the balance when the current flows is 1.5094 N. Determine the direction in which current flows through the top part of the wire. What is the size of this current? Calculate the magnitude of the force acting on the wire, stating its direction. What will the reading on the balance become if the direction of the magnetic field is reversed?

13.5 A solenoid 0.35 m long has 100 turns. Calculate the magnetic field strength inside it when a current of 4.2 A flows through it.

Chapter 14

14.1 Explain in detail why two parallel wires carrying currents in the same direction attract each other.

14.2 Calculate the magnetic field strength 4 cm from a wire carrying a current of 5 A. What is the field strength 8 cm from the same wire? A second wire, parallel to the first, carries a current of 8 A in the opposite direction. Calculate the force acting on the wires per unit length when they are 4 cm apart, and state its effect.

14.3 Define the *ampere*. Show how this definition also fixes the value of μ_0, the permeability of free space.

Chapter 15

15.1 Show how the expression for the magnetic force on a charged particle (Bqv) is derived from that for the magnetic force on a current-carrying wire (BIl).

15.2 Explain why a charged particle moving at 90° to a magnetic field follows a circular path. Suggest what shape of path is followed when moving at 70° to the field.

particle has a charge of $+3.2 \times 10^{-19}$ C 6.4×10^{-27} kg. Calculate the diameter of ...ollowed by an alpha particle moving at 1.8 × ... s^{-1} at 90° to a magnetic field of strength 120 mT.

15.4 What is a *mass spectrometer*? How does it work?

Chapter 16

16.1 State *Faraday's law* of electromagnetic induction.

16.2 A solenoid consists of 200 turns with an area of cross-section of 4 cm². It is quickly moved from a region where the magnetic field strength along its axis is 450 mT to one where it is 160 mT. If it takes 200 ms to move the solenoid, calculate the e.m.f. induced across its ends.

16.3 State *Lenz's law* of electromagnetic induction. Of what conservation law is Lenz's law a consequence?

Chapter 17

17.1 The diagram shows a gold ring on a silk thread about to swing through a magnetic field.

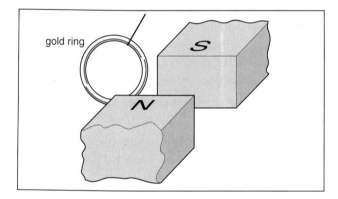

gold ring

S

N

Two students predict differently the influence of the magnetic field on the motion of the ring. Student A says that the effect of the field is to increase the speed of the ring as it enters the field and to slow it down as it leaves: the net effect is zero. Student B says there is only one effect: to slow the ring down. Which student is correct? Explain why the ring behaves as this student describes.

17.2 Some moving vehicles use an electromagnetic braking system. A disc attached to their wheels rotates near a large electromagnet. Explain why turning the electromagnet on slows the vehicle. Why can such a system not be used as the parking brake?

17.3 Calculate the e.m.f. induced across the metal handlebars as a student cycles to college at 12 m s⁻¹. The handlebars are 60 cm wide and the Earth's vertical magnetic field strength at this latitude is

5×10^{-5} T. Explain why no current flows through the student if he touches the metal parts of the handlebars.

Chapter 18

18.1 Explain why it is necessary to reverse the current through the coil of a motor every half turn. With the help of a diagram, explain how this reversal is achieved.

18.2 Sketch a graph showing how the e.m.f. induced across the ends of a coil rotating in a magnetic field varies with time. What happens if the coil is rotated faster?

18.3 The resistance of the rotating coil (armature) of a 12 V motor is 0.15 Ω. Calculate the current through this coil when it is stationary and connected to the 12 V supply. When the motor is running freely, a current of 3 A flows in it. Explain why the current has dropped. Sketch a graph to show how current varies with motor speed.

Chapter 19

19.1 A small clock has a pendulum 12 cm long swinging with an amplitude of 1.5 cm. Calculate its period, its maximum velocity and its maximum acceleration. Write equations that show how (a) the displacement, (b) the velocity and (c) the acceleration vary with time.

19.2 The voltage output from an oscillator varies with time such that $V = 6\cos(3000\pi t)$. Sketch a graph of this output, marking both axes with suitable scales. A 12 Ω resistor is connected across the terminals of the oscillator. Write down the equation for the time variation of the current in this resistor.

19.3 An alternating current flows in a 120 Ω resistor, the terminals of which are connected to an oscilloscope. The trace shows a vertical line of length 30 mm. The Y-gain is set at 0.5 mm V⁻¹. What is the peak-to-peak voltage across the resistor? Calculate the r.m.s. value of the alternating current. Describe how you would use the oscilloscope to determine the frequency of the alternating current.

Examination questions

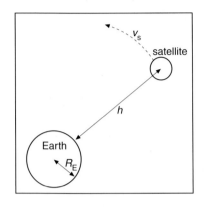

1 The diagram shows a satellite of mass m_s, in circular orbit at speed v_s around the Earth, mass M_E. The satellite is at a height h above the Earth's surface and the radius of the Earth is R_E. Using these symbols write down an expression for the centripetal force needed to maintain the satellite in this orbit. [2]

Write down an expression for the gravitational field strength in the region of the satellite. State an appropriate unit for this quantity. [3]

Use your two expressions to show that the greater the height of the satellite above the Earth, the smaller will be its orbital speed. [3]

Explain why, if a satellite slows down in its orbit, it nevertheless gradually spirals in towards the Earth's surface. [2]

2 What is meant by the term *gravitational potential V* at a point? In what unit is it measured? [3]

The gravitational potential at the surface of the Earth is given by the relationship $V = -GM/r$ where G is the universal constant of gravitation, M is the mass of the Earth and r is the radius of the Earth. Explain why V at the surface of the Earth is negative. [2]

Show that $g = GM/r^2$ where g is the acceleration of free fall close to the Earth. [1]

Use the relationships $V = -GM/r$ and $g = GM/r^2$ to help you to show that the escape speed for a projectile leaving the Earth is 11×10^3 m s^{-1}. [Radius of Earth = 6400 km] [3]

In calculating the escape speed for a space probe travelling outwards from the solar system what would the symbols M and r represent? [1]

3 Using the usual symbols write down an equation for (i) Newton's law of gravitation, (ii) Coulomb's law. [2]

State *one* difference and *one* similarity between gravitational and electric fields. [2]

A speck of dust has a mass of 1.0×10^{-18} kg and carries a charge equal to that of one electron. Near to the Earth's surface it experiences a uniform downward electric field of strength 100 N C^{-1} and a uniform gravitational field of strength 9.8 N kg^{-1}. Draw a free-body force diagram for the speck of dust. Label the forces clearly. Calculate the magnitude and direction of the resultant force on the speck of dust. [6]

4 The diagram shows two charged, parallel, conducting plates. Copy the diagram and add to it solid lines to show the electric field in the space between and just *beyond* the edges of the plates. [2]

Add to your diagram dotted lines to show *three* equipotentials in the same regions. [2]

5 Define *electric potential* at a point. Is electric potential a vector or a scalar quantity? [3]

An isolated charged conducting sphere has a radius *a*. The graph shows the variation of electric potential *V* with distance *r* from the centre of the sphere.

Make a copy of the graph. On it, mark with an 'a' on the distance axis the point that represents the radius of the sphere. Add to your graph a line showing how electric field strength *E* varies with distance for the same range of values of *r*. [4]

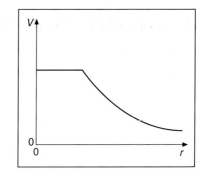

6 The circuit shown is used to investigate the discharge of a capacitor.

With the switch in position S_1 the capacitor is charged. The switch is then moved to S_2 and readings of current and time are taken as the capacitor discharges through the resistor. The results are plotted on the graph.

Calculate the maximum charge stored in the capacitor. [1]

Copy the graph. Make suitable calculations to enable you to add scales to both axes of your graph. [4]

A second 470 µF capacitor is connected in series with the original capacitor. The switch is moved back to S_1 to recharge the capacitors. State the new charge stored. [1]

The switch is moved to S_2 and another set of discharge readings is taken. Draw a second line on your graph to show how the current varies with time during this discharge. [2]

How could the charge stored in the capacitors be estimated from your graph? [1]

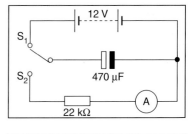

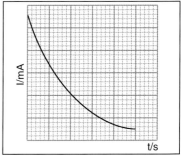

7 Explain what is meant by a *neutral point* in a field. [2]

The diagram shows two similar solenoids A and B. Solenoid A has twice the number of turns per metre. Solenoid A carries four times the current as B. Make a copy of the diagram, and on it draw the magnetic field lines in, around and between the two solenoids. [4]

If the distance between the centres of A and B is 1 m, estimate the position of the neutral point. Ignore the effect of the Earth's magnetic field. [3]

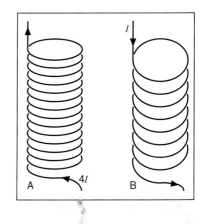

8 The magnitude of the force on a current-carrying conductor in a magnetic field is directly proportional to the magnitude of the current in the conductor. With the aid of a diagram describe how you could demonstrate this in a school laboratory. [4]

At a certain point on the Earth's surface the horizontal component of the Earth's magnetic field is 1.8×10^{-5} T. A straight piece of conducting wire 2.0 m long, of mass 1.5 g, lies on a horizontal wooden bench in an east–west direction. When a very large current flows momentarily in the wire it is just sufficient to cause the wire to lift up off the surface of the bench. State the direction of the current in the wire. Calculate the current. What other noticeable effect will this current produce? [4]

EXAMINATION QUESTIONS

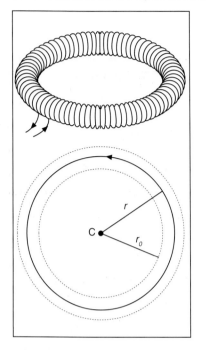

9 A child sleeps at an average distance of 30 cm from household wiring. The mains supply is 230 V r.m.s. Calculate the maximum possible magnetic flux density in the region of the child when the wire is transmitting 3.45 kW of power. [4]

Why might the magnetic field due to the current in the wire pose more of a health risk to the child than the Earth's magnetic field, given that they are of similar magnitudes? [2]

10 A toroid is a conducting wire wound in the shape of a torus (a doughnut). A toroid could be made by bending a slinky spring into a torus. The figure shows a toroid, together with a plan view to which one magnetic field line has been added.

Theory suggests that for a toroid of N turns, the magnetic flux density B within the coils of the toroid at a distance r from the centre C of the toroid is given by $B = \mu_0 NI/2\pi r$. Describe how you would verify this relationship using a precalibrated Hall probe. [6]

For distances $r < r_0$, suggest how B might vary with r. Give a reason for your answer. [2]

11 The permittivity of free space ε_0 has units F m^{-1}. The permeability of free space μ_0 has units N A^{-2}. Show that the units of $1/\sqrt{(\varepsilon_0\mu_0)}$ are m s^{-1}. [3]

Calculate the magnitude of $1/\sqrt{(\varepsilon_0\mu_0)}$. [1]

Comment on your answers. [1]

12 Explain what is meant by a *field* in physics. [2]

State *two* differences between electric and magnetic fields. [2]

A beam of electrons is accelerated from rest in an electric field of strength 8.5×10^5 N C^{-1}. Calculate the force on, and the acceleration of, each electron. [3]

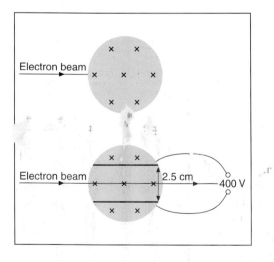

13 The diagrams show a beam of electrons, which have been accelerated by a potential difference V, travelling in an evacuated tube. A magnetic field acts at right angles to their direction of motion in the shaded region and into the plane of the paper.

Copy the first diagram and draw on it the path of the electrons in the shaded region. [2]

In the second diagram a pair of conducting plates, 2.5 cm apart, has been introduced into the shaded region. A potential difference is applied to the plates and is gradually increased until it reaches 400 V when the path of the electrons is a straight line. Copy this diagram, and on it indicate the polarity of the plates. [1]

Calculate the electric field strength in the region between the plates, and the force on an electron due to this field. [3]

The magnetic flux density in the shaded region is 1×10^{-3} T. Show that the speed of the electrons must be 1.6×10^7 m s^{-1}. [2]

Calculate the potential difference V required to accelerate electrons to this speed. [3]

14 The induction microphone, shown in the diagram, converts sound waves into electrical signals that can be amplified.

Describe the stages by which the sound waves are converted into electrical signals. State whether the signals are a.c. or d.c. [6]

If the alternating output from a signal generator were fed into the microphone, describe and explain what would happen to the diaphragm. [3]

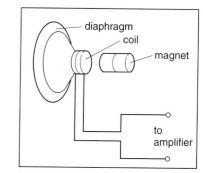

15 A light aluminium washer rests on the end of a solenoid as shown in the diagram.

A large direct current is switched on in the solenoid. Explain why the washer jumps and immediately falls back. [5]

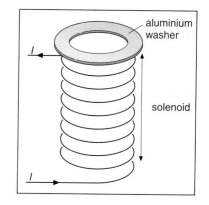

16 A simple pendulum has a period of 2.0 s and oscillates with an amplitude of 10 cm. What is the frequency of the oscillations? [1]

At what point of the swing is the speed of the pendulum bob a maximum? Calculate this maximum speed. [3]

At what points of the swing is the acceleration of the pendulum bob a maximum? Calculate this acceleration. [3]

17 One simple model of the hydrogen molecule assumes that it is composed of two oscillating hydrogen atoms joined by two springs as shown in the diagram.

If the spring constant of each spring is 1.13×10^3 N m^{-1}, and the mass of a hydrogen atom is 1.67×10^{-27} kg, show that the frequency of oscillation of a hydrogen atom is 1.31×10^{14} Hz. [2]

Using this spring model, discuss why light of wavelength 2.29×10^{-6} m would be strongly absorbed by the hydrogen molecule. [4]

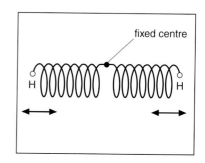

Solid Materials Topic

M1 The graph shows how the potential energy of a pair of atoms depends upon their separation.

What is the separation of the atoms when the force between them is zero? From this separation how much energy is required to free the atoms from each other? Assuming that the attractive force between separations of 3.05×10^{-10} m and 3.15×10^{-10} m remains constant, calculate the value of this force. If a pair of atoms at their equilibrium separation is given 10×10^{-21} J of vibrational energy, use the graph to find their new mean separation. Explain your reasoning. [8]

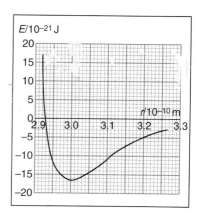

acting on it. Given that the density of wood is 600 kg m⁻³ and the density of glycerine is 800 kg m⁻³, draw a scale diagram of how the two cylinders would appear when floating vertically next to each other in a large beaker of glycerine. [3]

What is meant by the term *isostasy*? Describe how the floating cylinders can be used as a simple model of the principle of isostasy. State *one* piece of evidence that supports the principle of isostasy. [7]

Age/10⁶ years	I/deg
less than 1	69
of the order of 50	61
of the order of 220	50
of the order of 300	0

E5 The angle of declination (dip) I is the angle between the direction of the Earth's magnetic field and its horizontal component at the same point. I is related to latitude L by the equation, $\tan I = 2 \tan L$. The table gives the values of I for rocks of different ages found in Great Britain.

Estimate the latitude of Great Britain at the present time. What do these results suggest about the position of Great Britain over the last 300 million years? [4]

E6 List the *four* principal layers of the atmosphere in order from the Earth's surface upwards. Within each of these layers, state how the temperature varies with height. [4]

E7 At constant temperature the pressure of the atmosphere decreases exponentially with height according to the equation $p = p_0 e^{-kh}$, where p_0 is the pressure at the Earth's surface. Given that p at a height of 5 km is approximately $\frac{1}{2}p_0$, estimate the height at which p will have fallen to $\frac{1}{8}p_0$. [2]

E8 The graph shows the relative intensity of the energy distribution in the spectrum of a body radiating at a temperature of 5900 K (the approximate temperature of the Sun).

State *two* ways in which the spectrum of a body radiating at a temperature of 286 K (the approximate temperature of the Earth) differs from the one shown. State *Wien's law* and use it to calculate the wavelength at which the intensity of radiation from the Earth is a maximum. [6]

Different molecules in the Earth's atmosphere absorb energy strongly at different wavelengths. The table gives approximate values of some of these wavelengths for certain molecules.

Discuss how the presence of water vapour, carbon dioxide and ozone in the Earth's atmosphere affects (a) the radiation received from the Sun at the surface of the Earth, and (b) the equilibrium temperature reached by the Earth. [5]

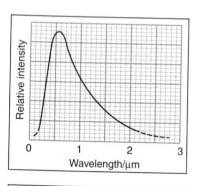

Molecule	Absorbed wavelength /μm
water vapour	6
carbon dioxide	15
ozone	0.3

E9 Draw a diagram to illustrate the simple three-cell model of atmospheric circulation in the Northern hemisphere. Label clearly the Hadley and polar cells and show the direction of circulation in each. Describe the mechanism responsible for the Hadley cell. [7]

Particle Physics Topic

P1 Sketch a graph showing the energy spectrum of β- particles emitted during β- decay. Explain in detail why the shape of this graph led to the prediction of the existence of the neutrino. [7]

P2 Calculate the force of repulsion between two protons separated by a distance of 1.0×10^{-14} m in an atomic nucleus. [2]

The Rutherford scattering experiment was used to investigate the structure of the atom. Deep inelastic scattering provided evidence about the structure of protons and neutrons. Outline the similarities and differences between these two experiments. What conclusion was drawn from the deep inelastic scattering experiment? [7]

The quarks in a nucleon are held together by the strong interaction. What exchange particle mediates this interaction? State the mass and charge of this exchange particle. What evidence is there that the range of this exchange particle is less than 10^{-14} m? [4]

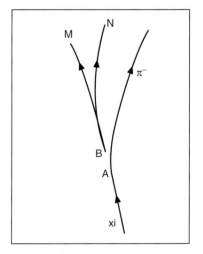

P3 The tracks associated with one particular interaction in a hydrogen bubble chamber are shown in the diagram.

These tracks show a xi particle travelling through the bubble chamber and decaying at A into a lambda particle and a negative pion. What can you deduce about the charge on the lambda and on the xi? Explain how you reached this conclusion. The lambda particle produced at A subsequently decays at B into another pair of particles, a proton and a pion. Which particle (M or N) is the proton? Explain how you arrived at your answer. [6]

P4 In a head-on collision between two protons of equal kinetic energy the following interaction was observed:

$$p + p \rightarrow p + 7\pi^+ + 7\pi^- + K^+ + \Lambda$$

Data: mass of p = 938 MeV/c^2, mass of π^+ or π^- = 140 MeV/c^2, mass of K^+ = 494 MeV/c^2 and mass of Λ = 1115 MeV/c^2.

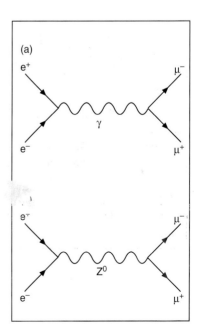

Calculate the minimum kinetic energy in MeV of each proton for this interaction to occur. Explain why this is the minimum possible value. Why would this interaction not be observed if one of the protons were stationary and the other had twice your calculated minimum kinetic energy. [6]

P5 An electron and a positron can annihilate by either of the mechanisms shown in the diagram.

Which of the fundamental interactions is represented by each figure? Which figure illustrates the most frequent mechanism electron–positron annihilation? Why is the interaction shown in (b) short range compared to that shown in (a)? Draw another diagram to illustrate the exchange of a π^+ between a neutron and a proton. [7]

103

EXAMINATION QUESTIONS

P6 Use the laws of conservation of lepton number, baryon number and charge to decide whether each of the following reactions is or is not possible. Show clearly how you applied the laws in each case. Both p and K particles are mesons. [6]

$$p + \bar{p} \rightarrow 4\pi^+ + 4\pi^-$$

$$K^0 \rightarrow \pi^+ + \pi^-$$

$$\pi^0 \rightarrow e^- + \bar{\nu}_e$$

P7 A Σ^+ decays with a lifetime of approximately 10^{-10} s as follows:

$$\Sigma^+ \rightarrow p + \pi^0$$

The quark structures of the particles involved are:

$$\Sigma^+ \text{ (uus)} \qquad p \text{ (uud)} \qquad \pi^0 \text{ (u}\bar{\text{u}}\text{)}$$

What type of interaction must be responsible for this decay? Give *two* pieces of evidence to support your answer. What exchange particles might be involved in the decay? Why does this interaction only operate over a very short range? [6]

P8 State *one* piece of evidence that supports the Big Bang theory and explain how it does so. The very early universe was made up of a collection of quarks, leptons and exchange particles. Through what stages has it passed in order to reach its present state? Explain why atoms were unstable when the universe was at a temperature greater than about 4000 K. [7]

P9 A partially inflated balloon has three dots, A, B and C, drawn on its surface as shown in the diagram.

Redraw the balloon, as it will appear when fully inflated. Discuss the ways in which this balloon can be used as a model for an expanding universe. Describe how it may be helpful for explaining Hubble's law. [8]

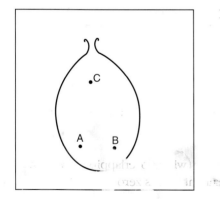

Things you need to know

Chapter 1

mass: amount of matter in a body

weight: gravitational force from Earth acting on a body

field (or **force field**): region in which a force acts

gravitational field: region where gravitational forces are exerted on a mass

gravitational field strength: force exerted by a gravitational field on each kilogram

Chapter 2

Newton's law of gravitation: gravitational force between two bodies is directly proportional to the product of their masses and inversely proportional to the square of their separation ($F = GmM/r^2$)

universal gravitational constant: the constant that applies in all situations of gravitational attraction

Chapter 3

geostationary (or **geosynchronous**) **satellite:** orbits above the equator with a period of 24 h and thus maintains the same position above the Earth's surface

Chapter 4

inverse square law: when a quantity decreases in proportion to the square of the increasing distance

Chapter 5

gravitational potential difference: difference in potential energy per kilogram between two points

gravitational potential at a point: difference in potential energy between that point and infinity

escape speed: ertical speed required to totally leav the gravitational influence of the Earth

Chapter 6

Coulomb's law: force between two charges is directly proportional to the product of their charges and inversely proportional to the square of their separation ($F = kqQ/r^2$)

Chapter 7

electric field: region where there are electric forces on charges

electric field strength: force exerted by an electric field on each coulomb

electron gun: device for producing and projecting a beam of electrons

thermionic emission: the freeing of electrons from a metal due to increased thermal vibration of the lattice

Chapter 8

equipotential: line joining points of equal potential energy

potential gradient: rate at which potential difference changes with distance

Chapter 9

time constant: time for capacitor's charge and potential difference to decrease to 1/e of its original value

Chapter 10

magnetic field: region where magnetic forces are experienced

neutral point: position within ove ing magnetic fields where the resultar t field i

domain: a group of atoms with their magnetic fields aligned

THINGS YOU NEED TO KNOW

Chapter 11
corkscrew rule: the magnetic field is clockwise around a wire carrying a current away from you

solenoid: a cylindrical current-carrying coil of wire with a large number of turns

Chapter 12
Fleming's left-hand rule: using your left hand – first finger shows direction of magnetic field, second finger current and thumb the thrust (or force) on the conductor

Chapter 13
magnetic flux density: a measure of the strength of a magnetic field

tesla: unit of magnetic flux density, where 1 T produces a force of 1 N on each metre length of wire carrying a current of 1 A perpendicular to the magnetic field

Hall probe: device for comparing magnetic flux densities of steady fields

Chapter 14
one ampere: that constant current which, when flowing through two infinitely long parallel straight conductors of negligible cross-section placed 1 m apart in a vacuum, produces a force per unit length between them of 2×10^{-7} N m^{-1}

Chapter 15
mass spectrometer: instrument that uses the motion of charged particles in a magnetic field to separate charged particles according to their mass

Chapter 16
magnetic flux through an area: total amount of magnetism through that area, equal to the product of the magnetic flux density and the area

magnetic flux linkage: product of magnetic flux and the number of turns

Faraday's law: magnitude of induced e.m.f. in a circuit is directly proportional to the rate of change of magnetic flux linkage through that circuit

Lenz's law: any current driven by an induced e.m.f. opposes the change causing it

Chapter 19
simple harmonic motion (s.h.m.): oscillatory motion where the period does not depend on the amplitude

definition of s.h.m.: motion where the acceleration (or force) is directly proportional to the displacement from a fixed point and always directed towards that point

sinusoidal: shape (either sine or cosine) of the time trace associated with s.h.m.

Equations to learn

Electric force between two charges q and Q

$$F = kqQ/r^2$$

where for free space (or air) $k = 1/(4\pi\varepsilon_0)$

Gravitational force between two masses m and M

$$F = GmM/r^2$$

Index

INDEX